Exam Skills Practice

Edexcel GCSE Geography B: Evolving Planet

Extend

Student Workbook

Nigel Yates and David Holmes

ALWAYS LEARNING

PEARSON

Contents

About this book

This workbook has been written to help you practise your exam skills as you prepare for your GCSE Geography B exams for Unit 1 and Unit 2. You'll find practice for each question type in each unit, helping you to understand what the examiner will be looking for in top-level answers. You'll also find answers to the activities at the back of the book, so that you can check whether you're on track after you've completed the activities.

Unit 3, 'Making geographical decisions' is based on a resource booklet that you will study in class. The topic changes each year but the skills that you need to answer the questions in the exam remain largely the same each year. Many of these skills are exactly those that you need to do well on in the other two units and are skills that are covered in this book. Others, more directed to Unit 3 in particular, are covered extensively in your *Edexcel GCSE Geography B: Evolving Planet Student Book* ISBN: 9781846905018.

Introduction

Unit 1: Dynamic planet

There are three sections in Unit 1, and eight topics within these sections. You must answer questions on **six** topics. In this workbook, the Unit 1 topics have been colour-coded to help you quickly find the ones relevant to you. In the exam, though, you'll need to make sure you know which sections you've studied so that you can go straight to them and not waste time looking at questions for other sections.

- Section A covers: Restless Earth; Climate and change; Battle for the biosphere and Water world. All four topics are compulsory and you will need to answer all the questions in section A. Each topic is worth 8 marks.
- Section B covers: Coastal change and conflict and River processes and pressures. You choose one topic and answer one question based on your chosen topic. Each question is worth 9 marks.
- Section C covers: Oceans on the edge and Extreme climates. You choose one topic and answer one question based on your chosen topic. Each question is worth 9 marks.

You'll find guidance on each of these question types on pages 4–11.

Unit 2: People and the planet

There are three sections in Unit 2, and eight topics within these sections. You must answer questions on **six** topics. Again, the Unit 2 topics have been colour-coded to help you quickly find the ones relevant to you. In the exam, though, you'll need to make sure you know which sections you've studied so that you can go straight to them and not waste time looking at questions for other sections.

- Section A covers: Population dynamics; Consuming resources; Living spaces and Making a living. All four topics are compulsory and you will need to answer all the questions in section A. Each topic is worth 8 marks.
- Section B covers: Changing cities and Changing countryside. You choose one topic and answer one question based on your chosen topic. Each question is worth 9 marks.
- Section C covers: Development dilemmas and World of work. You choose one topic and answer one question based on your chosen topic. Each question is worth 9 marks.

You'll find guidance on each of these question types on pages 4–11.

Understanding the exam

Introduction to Unit 1 and Unit 2

Your unit 1 exam will test your knowledge of the **Dynamic planet**.

Your unit 2 exam will test your knowledge of **People and the planet**.

In each exam you will have the following types of questions:

- Section A: Questions on the four compulsory topics (Topics 1 to 4) worth a total of 8 marks for each topic.
- Sections B and C: Questions on the optional topics in Section B (Topics 5 or 6) and C (Topics 7 or 8). You choose one topic from each section depending on what you've covered in class. You answer one question on each topic and it is worth 9 marks.

Make sure that you know which topics you have covered!

Highlight the optional topics you are covering and cross through the topics in the workbook you are not studying.

Unit 1 Dynamic planet

Section A (compulsory topics)

Topic 1 Restless Earth

Topic 2 Climate and change

Topic 3 Battle for the biosphere

Topic 4 Water world

Section B (optional topics)

Topic 5 Coastal change and conflict

Topic 6 River processes and pressures

Section C (optional topics)

Topic 7 Oceans on the edge

Topic 8 Extreme climates

Unit 2 People and the planet

Section A (compulsory topics)

Topic 1 Population dynamics

Topic 2 Consuming resources

Topic 3 Living spaces

Topic 4 Making a living

Section B (optional topics)

Topic 5 Changing cities

Topic 6 Changing countryside

Section C (optional topics)

Topic 7 Development dilemmas

Topic 8 World of work

Watching the clock

You have 60 minutes for both papers and there are 50 marks to be won. That means just over 1 minute for each mark. The shortest, 1-mark questions will probably not take you a minute because they do not require a full sentence but just a few words. This will leave you a little longer for the longer answers. The 2-mark answers will need between one word or phrase to two or even three sentences and the 4- and 6-mark questions will need as many as five to eight sentences to answer.

Give yourself a few minutes at the end to read over your answers. Nobody is at their most efficient in an exam and we all make silly mistakes.

Remember

Remember, you can't lose marks so only cross answers out if you are absolutely sure that you are replacing them with something better!

Types of question

All the questions are divided into at least three parts (a), (b), (c), and sometimes four (d). It is useful for you to understand what these questions are designed to test.

The (a) part of the question is usually

- worth 1 or sometimes 2 marks
- a skill such as reading a graph, table or map
- a skill such as interpreting a photograph or cartoon.

> **Hint**
> If in any doubt then have an intelligent guess – NEVER LEAVE BLANKS.
> One mark means one answer – don't put two!

The (b) part of the question is not linked to the (a) part

- It may be a definition.
- It may ask to 'Describe', 'Explain, 'Outline' or 'Suggest'.
- It is almost always worth 2 marks.

> **Hint**
> 1. For 2 marks say two basic things or one in more depth by adding detail, evidence or perhaps an example.
> 2. In a 2-mark question it may tell you to:
>   *(b) Describe* ***two*** *… (2)* This question requires two basic points.
>   *(b) Describe how … (2)* This question requires one basic point that is developed by adding detail, evidence or an example.
> 3. If in doubt say three things.
> 4. Use an example to support your point if appropriate – you are all able to do this.

The (c)/(d) parts of the question

- There can be either a (c) or (d) part.
- Is usually worth 4 marks for the questions on the first four topics.
- Is always worth 6 marks for the questions on topics 5, 6 ,7 and 8.
- It often asks you to explain something.
- It may involve you using facts and figures from a 'case study' as in 'For a named country' to support a point and add extra detail to get higher marks. This will help support the basic point and often get an extra mark.

> **Hint**
> There can sometimes be two separate (b) bits instead of a (c)/(d) bit!

Picking apart the question

Like a modelling kit every question is made up of a number of bits that fit together. Have a look at this question.

Using examples, explain why some governments wish to control population growth.

Command word: The word highlighted in yellow is the command word. It tells you what to do!

Restriction: The word in blue is a restriction. It narrows down the focus a bit further so in this case it tells you that you must talk about why **governments** wish to control population growth – not why your friends want to or why you want to!

Focus: The words in pink identify the focus of the question – not just about population growth but about the control of that growth.

Topic: The words highlighted in green tell you which topic is being questioned.

Command words

There are a limited number of command words that will be used. The commonest are:

- State – give a very brief view of something
- Name – identify something
- Identify – name something
- Outline – give a few details about something or perhaps briefly explain a process
- Define – give the meaning of a geographical term or expression
- Describe – give details of something
- Explain – show how something works, the processes that take place
- Suggest – offer an idea or explanation about something

Topics

The topic is the area of the syllabus being tested. This rarely causes any problem because the papers are already divided into topics! Just be careful that you have chosen the right options in Sections B and C.

Focus

This does cause some problems. Have a quick look at the question below:

Explain why some governments might wish to control the number of migrants entering their country.

1. Which of the following student answers has the right 'focus'? Tick your choice then check the answer on page 106.
   - A There are many ways of controlling migration. Governments can use quotas and skills tests to control the number of people entering the country. ☐
   - B The government may be worried about unemployment levels or perhaps there is racism in the population that will make it difficult to accept too many migrants. ☐
2. Now you have identified the answer with the right 'focus', try writing a question that matches the 'wrong' answer. What question was this student answering?

Restrictions

Not all questions have 'restrictions' that narrow the focus even more but quite a few do so watch out for them.

1. Have a look at the following questions and see if you can spot the restrictions. Highlight them.
   - a) *Using examples, explain how the 'new economy' is affecting developed countries.*
   - b) *Describe how climate change in the past affected people and ecosystems.*
2. Some restrictions are quite easy to miss; they might be 'little' words such as 'rate' or 'pattern'. Look at the following question and see if you can spot the two-word phrase that many students might miss! Highlight it.

   Describe one way in which employment change in a rapidly growing city has affected the environment.

Putting it into practice

Read the two example questions below and then look at the marks for each question.

Example A *State two characteristics of oceanic crust. (2)*

Example B *Outline two ways in which buildings can be made more resistant to earthquakes. (4)*

1. How much would you expect to write in your answer? Complete the table for each example.

	Example A	Example B
Two sentences		
A paragraph		
Two or three paragraphs		

2. How long do you think you should spend answering the questions? Complete the table for each example.

	Example A	Example B
Less than 1 minute		
2–3 minutes		
4–5 minutes		

3. For the two questions above, identify the command word and the focus. Complete the table.

	Example A	Example B
Command word		
Focus		

4. Now decide what type of question it is. You may choose from: a **describe** question, an **explain** question or a **define** question. Describe what this means.

   Example A is a .... question. This means ....

   Example B is a .... question. This means ....

What questions are designed to test

There are several different types of questions asked which are designed to test:

- Your geographical **skills** – for example, you may be given a resource such as a map or a photograph of a place that you have never heard of, let alone studied. It is not what you know about the place that is being tested, it is your ability to apply your skills to make some sense of what the map, photograph or diagram shows – that is the skill! This might mean reading a graph, table or map, or perhaps interpreting a photograph or cartoon.
- Your **knowledge and understanding** of the topic – this is based on your factual recall; how much detail you remember about each topic. These questions may ask for a definition of a key term or ask for some detail about a case study or example that you have learnt.
- Your **application** of that knowledge and understanding – this involves your ability to interpret questions correctly and apply your knowledge effectively to answer them. So it's not just what you know but which bits you select to illustrate your understanding.

What are geographical skills questions?

The skills questions are always found at the beginning of each topic in Unit 1 and Unit 2. They are usually the (a) (i) and (a) (ii) questions and are worth 2 or 3 marks so up to 12 marks for the whole paper.

These questions will ask you to use your skills to make sense and interpret information from, for example:

- maps
- photographs
- drawings and cartoons
- tables and graphs.

Hint

Just occasionally, one of these (a) questions will be a test of your knowledge and understanding. (Improving your answers to these skills questions will be dealt with on pages 12–19.)

Quality of written communication

Sometimes there are skills marks awarded for your ability to construct longer 6-mark answers in the questions in Sections B and C. These questions are marked with an * and include credit for what is called 'quality of written communication' (QWC for short). The skills that you need to answer these questions will be investigated on page 10.

How do I answer knowledge-based questions?

Somewhere between 30 and 40 marks on each of the exam papers are made up of questions based on your knowledge and understanding of a topic and how well you can apply this. These range from 1-mark questions to 6-mark questions.

1-mark questions

Single-mark questions frequently use command words such as:

State… Identify… Give… Define…

The mark schemes for these single-mark questions are usually three possible 'right' answers.

Hint

One important tip is that if you have forgotten an answer, e.g. an example of 'a constructive margin', then make a guess. Blank spaces **never** get marks – but **sometimes** you get lucky!

2–3 mark questions

Some 2-mark questions will ask you to:

State ***two****…* or *Identify* ***two****…*

In these cases mark schemes will expect two basic points without any development.

However, most of the longer 2-, 3- and 4-mark questions have more flexible mark schemes meaning that there may be several different ways of getting full marks.

Look at this example question.

For a named country suggest one possible impact of higher global temperatures. (2)

Now look at these student answers.

Student answers	
A	Sea-levels might rise and this will have harmful effects on many people.
B	Sea-levels will rise drowning agricultural land in regions such as East Anglia.
C	Sea-levels will rise because of melting ice caps in Greenland and Antarctica.

Each of the answers has a basic point which is worth 1 mark. The mark scheme gives several possible 'basic points' that could be used to gain one mark. As only one example is asked for, the second mark comes from an extension or development of that basic point, which means explaining the point further.

Mark scheme

Changes to sea-level (1) with impact on low-lying areas or coastal cities outlined. (1)

Changes to agriculture (1) different crops/livestock outlined. (1)

Changes to ecosystems/biomes (1) with impact on their productivity/utility to populations outlined. (1)

Changes to employment/work patterns (1) some jobs in decline/others growing outlined. (1)

Allow any other realistic change (1) with suitable development through a clearly identified impact. (1)

In this mark scheme the basic points are shown in green and the extensions or developments in blue. For example, 'Changes to sea-level' is the basic point which could be extended/developed by adding some detail on how this rising sea-level has affected a particular area.

Using the mark scheme, give the student answers a mark.

A .... B .... C ....

Hint

Things to watch include:

- The number of points you are supposed to make. For example, *'Describe **one** way...'* or *'Explain **two** impacts of...'*
- Some questions may only hint at the number of points you are supposed to make. For example, *'Describe the ways...'*. In this case more than one point is obviously sensible.
- Some questions will provide you with specific places to write your answer, for example: *'Describe **two** ways...*

  1 .... 2 ....

Common student answer errors

1. Not obeying the command word, for example, 'describing' when asked to 'explain' or the other way around is a common error made by students.
2. Misreading the question. Look at the following example:

*Outline **two** ways in which local governments can help reduce the use of cars in cities.*

How might answers to this go wrong?

- Missing **two ways** and giving more ways or less ways – more ways is not as much of a problem because it will all be marked.
- Missing the **focus**, the focus in this question is the reduction of car use.
- Missing the **restriction**, the restriction in this question is **local governments**. This does not mean individuals or **central** government.

Hint

When reading questions, work out the command word, topic and restriction before you get started.

4-mark questions

The same principles apply for 4-mark questions as for 2-mark questions.

- If the question asks for **two** reasons then answer it as though it was 2 × 2 marks. That is 2 marks for each separate idea, one for a basic point, one for development.
- If the question is open ended as in *'Describe the...'* or *'Explain why...'* you can take the same route as if **two** reasons had been asked for or give one reason/description with three points of detail or depth as extensions of that basic idea.

Look at the example question below.

Describe the changes in employment that take place as countries develop. (4)

Mark scheme

One mark for each basic point and a second mark for any of those points that are extended or developed. You can often do this with an example or just by adding a bit more detail to your basic point.

The changing types of employment – primary reducing throughout the process (1) secondary increasing and then falling (1) tertiary rising throughout the process (1) quaternary emerging in post-industrial societies (may mention changes in part-time/ full time (temporary (1) and female labour(1))

any point can be extended by example. (2)

The mark scheme shows that there are several routes to 4 marks – either covering a range of basic points, or giving two basic points with each of them developed/extended with a good example or a bit of detail.

1. Look at the following answer to the same question and give it a mark.

   Agriculture and other primary industries decline but secondary industry gets more important before it declines fast. In the last few years quaternary industries have grown up, these industries are to do with IT and research. Mark...........................

2. Now show where the marks came from by highlighting or underlining the answer, using green for any basic points and blue for any extensions or developments.

6-mark questions

The most challenging questions that you will answer are the extended writing in Sections B and C of both units. These questions

- make up 12 out of the 50 marks for the paper.
- are more testing because they expect you to construct an answer and not just write down everything that you know.
- are marked using different 'levels' rather than 'points'.

The mark schemes include some information about the likely ideas that students will cover and then a description of what each level might be like.

One of the ways in which examiners decide in which level your answer belongs is how well structured your answer is – does it have a beginning, a middle and a clear concluding point – a mini-essay almost? This is the 'quality of written communication' shown with an *. This also includes the quality of your spelling and grammar and use of correct geographical terminology, so pay particular attention to these as you write and check your answer.

The 'rules' of question-setting are the same as for the 1- 2- and 4-mark questions and they will almost always begin with 'describe' or, more likely, 'explain' commands but you might also be expected to include some case-study evidence too.

The mark scheme for 6-mark questions

A typical mark scheme will include a list of points that you might include – this is called the 'indicative content' and a set of 'descriptors' showing examiners what they should look out for at each level.

Because these are the hardest questions on the paper it is easy to lose a mark or two on these questions. In order to try and achieve the highest marks, the trick is to get into Level 3.

A typical Level 3 descriptor is shown below:

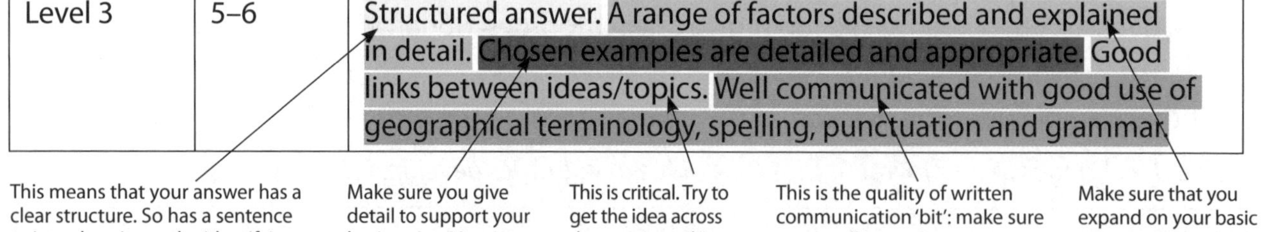

Level 3	5–6	Structured answer. A range of factors described and explained in detail. Chosen examples are detailed and appropriate. Good links between ideas/topics. Well communicated with good use of geographical terminology, spelling, punctuation and grammar.

This means that your answer has a clear structure. So has a sentence to introduce it, maybe identifying the case study. A 'middle' in which you offer two or, even better three different points and a conclusion in which you draw it together.

Make sure you give detail to support your basic point. Mention at least two specific facts and/or figures about the topic that correctly support your point.

This is critical. Try to get the idea across that not everything may work, some people don't agree, not all processes have the same effect.

This is the quality of written communication 'bit': make sure your spelling and grammar are good. Use geographical terms: 'abrasion' rather than 'wearing away like sandpaper'; 'developing country' rather than 'poor country'.

Make sure that you expand on your basic point by explaining clearly and giving detail. Generally explanation is the key bit – why is it as it is – aim for at least three points.

Maximising your marks on these questions is about trying to get beyond making simple statements – show that you can add more depth and explanation and that you can evaluate by balancing one point with another rather like a mini-debate. See the following examples:

Simple statements	Developed statements
Developing countries are poorer	There are many more people in developing countries but also a rich minority
Hard engineering is expensive and fails	Some hard engineering schemes are very expensive and may not be sustainable because…

Evaluation

Some questions will nudge you to 'come to a view' about an issue to access the highest marks. This 'nudge' will often come in the form of a phrase such as 'advantages and disadvantages', 'positive and negative', 'challenges and opportunities'. This means you will be expected to look at the 'fors' and 'againsts'. For example you might be expected to examine the advantages and disadvantages of:

- Hard and soft engineering
- Top down and bottom up development
- TNCs for the countries in which they operate

1. Look at the following student answers to this question.
   Examine the advantages and disadvantages of Transnational Corporations for the countries in which they operate. (6)

Student answers	
A	TNCs are very large businesses that set up factories in developing countries because of advantages like cheap labour. This provides jobs for the country. The workers will have more money to spend and the economy will be boosted. This has happened with Nike workers in Vietnam. Some TNCs will also bring different opportunities such as new types of goods; McDonalds operate in many countries giving consumers choices. There are some disadvantages too; in India the Coca Cola company uses large quantities of water in Kerala and this is not available to local farmers. Some of the jobs are not well paid such as those in the textile industry in Jamaica where firms such as Sara Lee had factories. What was worse was that these factories did not emply local women but used foreign labour.
B	TNCs are very large businesses who set up in developing countries because they can save money by employing cheap labour. They do create jobs as Nike has done in Vietnam but often wages are so low the amount of money workers have to spend is very small and the advantage is reduced. In some cases such as Sara Lee in Jamaica the benefit is even less because foreign labour is used. Comanies may provide new goods and services for a country such as McDonalds or Coca Cola in Kerala, India but a disadvantage is that they have a negative impact on resources such as water supplies. So some people and groups gain advantages whilst other people only put up with the disadvantages.

Use a highlighter to pick out key words and phrases that show where the student is trying to evaluate by balancing evidence from both sides of the 'debate'.

2. Which is the better answer and why?

....

....

Hint

Have they correctly identified the command word, focus and topic?
How many basic points have they made?
Have they given any development of these basic points/how much?
Have they used correct geographical terminology?
Have they got a clear structure?
Have they evaluated?

Now look at this answer with the examiner's comments added:

TNCs bring jobs to poorer countries as with Nike in Vietnam. The wages are quite high by local standards and the workers can save money and pay for education for their children. This can be a starting point for development as in Taiwan where large companies such as Acer started from quite small workshops making cheap goods for export. However, TNCs do not show much loyalty to countries and often shut down factories just because costs are lower elsewhere. This happened with Mattel making Barbie dolls around the Pacific. They can also be guilty of breaking rules about pollution and labour rules as well as destroying the environment as with Shell in the Niger delta.

Good range of advantages and disadvantages; described but also some explanation.

Good way of comparing advantages and disadvantages.

Case studies are used to support points.

Answer has a start, middle and end so is well structured.

Developing geographical skills

The (a) part of each question is a test of your ability to interpret a resource. For example, you may be given a photograph of a place that you have never heard of, let alone studied. It is not what you know about the place that is being tested, it is your ability to apply what you do know and make some sense of what the photograph shows – that is the skill!

The resource may be a map, a photograph, a graph or diagram and sometimes a cartoon or sketch.

These exercises are designed to help you develop these geographical skills and understand how the questions are marked.

Activity 1: How skills questions are marked

Almost all the skills questions will be 1- or 2-mark questions. The 2-mark questions usually reward a basic point with one mark and the second mark often comes from a development or extension of that basic idea or, sometimes, an example.

Study Figure 1 and then look at the question below.

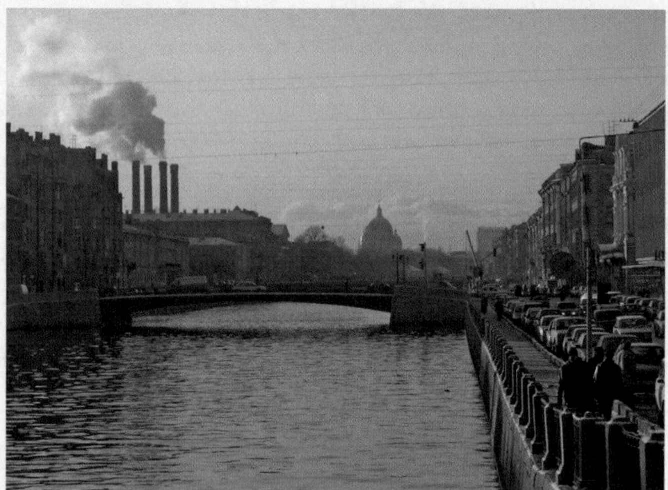

Figure 1 St Petersburg, Russia

Hint

Look back at pages 8–9 to remind yourself about making basic points and developing points.

Outline why this living space may have poor air quality. (2)

Look at the following student answers.

	Student answers	Mark
A	Because it is polluted.	1
B	Because the power station and cars will make it polluted.	2

The first answer is a 1-mark answer because it has the basic idea about 'pollution'; the second answer extends that idea by identifying two possible sources of that pollution and would therefore gain maximum marks.

Now look at the following answers. These answers have been awarded 0, 1 and 2 marks. Identify which is which and add the marks to the table.

	Student answers	Mark
A	It is in the city which is always dirty because of factories.	
B	Cars create fumes such as carbon monoxide.	
C	There are too many people about.	

Activity 2: Map skills

1. Study Figure 2 and then look at the question below.

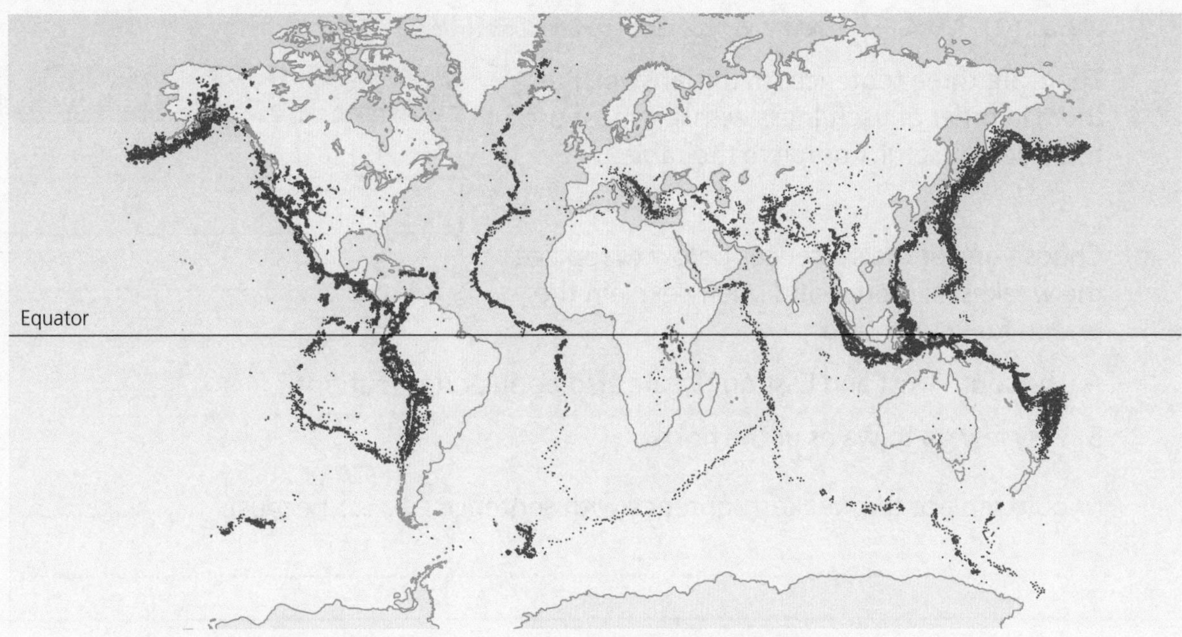

Figure 2 Global distribution of earthquakes (as shown by red dots)

Describe the pattern of earthquakes. (2)

Read the following student answers. Indicate with a tick the one which is worth 2 marks.

Student answers		Tick
A	There are many earthquakes all together in bunches on the land but hardly any out in the oceans.	
B	The pattern is very uneven with earthquakes occurring in distinct lines.	

2. Study Figure 3 and then look at the question below.

*Identify **one** region with many more retired people leaving than arriving. (1)*

Read the following student answers and indicate which one is incorrect by highlighting it in green.

Student answers	
A	Greater London and outer metropolitan
B	South west
C	Outer South East
D	East Anglia

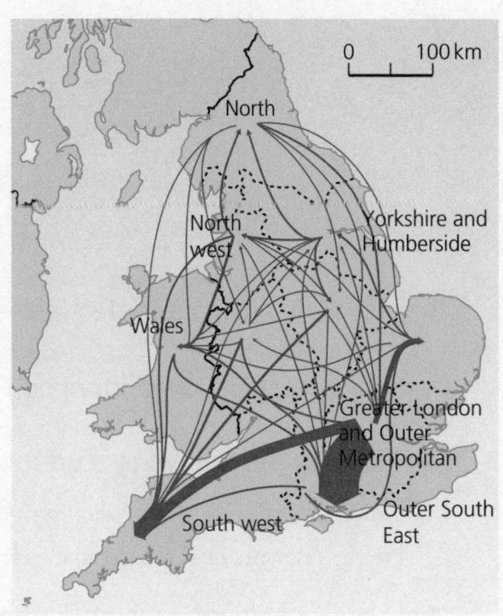

Figure 3 Retirement migration flows in England and Wales

3. a) Now look at this question and read the following student answer.

Describe where Londoners choose to move when they retire. (2)

Many Londoners leave the city when they retire. (1) They go to lots of different places. (2) Most of them go to the outer south east. (3)

There are three sentences in this answer. Put them in order of usefulness with 1 = most useful to 3 = least useful. Complete the table.

Sentence	Order of usefulness
1	
2	
3	

b) Choose one of the sentences below to replace the weakest sentence and briefly explain the reason for your choice.

A The south west and East Anglia are also popular destinations.

B Very few go to Wales or the north.

I would replace the weakest sentence with sentence .... because ....

....

Activity 3: Drawings and diagrams

1. Study Figure 4 and then look at the question below.

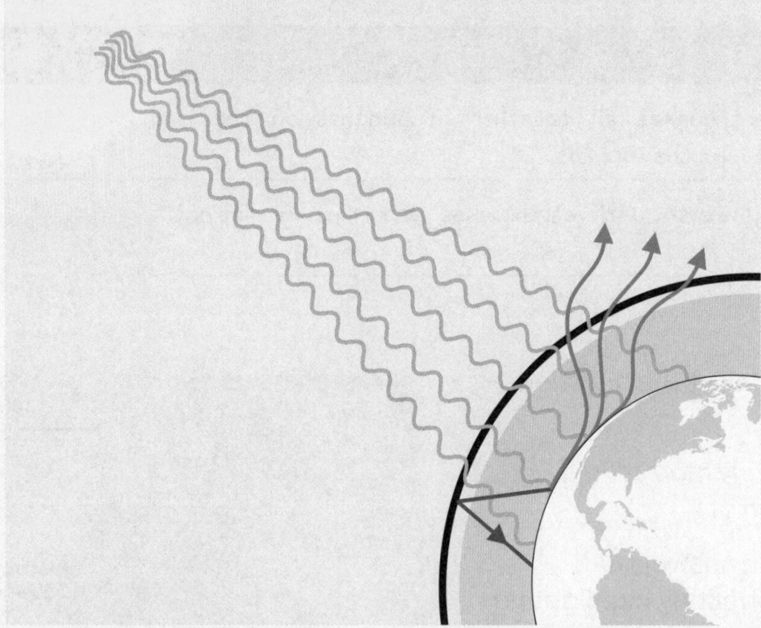

Figure 4 Heat energy radiated by the Earth

*Describe **two** things that happen to heat energy radiated by the Earth. (2)*

Now look at the following student answer. Why does this only deserve **1** mark?

1. Heat energy is absorbed by CO_2.
2. Heat energy heats up the atmosphere.

This answer only deserves 1 mark because ....

....

2. Tick one of the following sentences that would earn the answer a second mark.

A Heat energy is absorbed by the Earth ☐

B Heat energy goes back to the Sun ☐

C Heat energy escapes into space ☐

3. Identify the process being shown on Figure 4 then look at the following students answers. Tick the correct answer.

Student answers		Tick
A	Global warming	
B	The greenhouse effect	
C	Convection	

4. a) Study Figure 5 and then look at the question below.

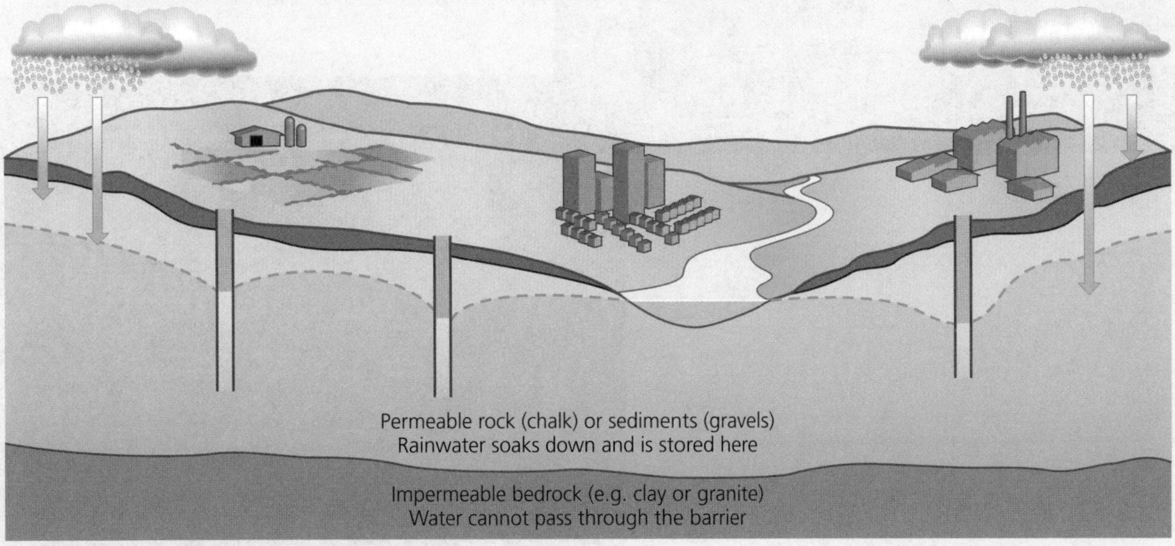

Figure 5 The features of an aquifer

Describe the impact of wells on the ground water. (1)

Now read the following student answers.

Student answers	
A	Where the wells are there is less water.
B	Where the wells are the water table is lower.
C	There is less water in the places where they have put the wells which is a mistake.

Two of these answers get the mark. Identify the answer that does not and briefly explain why.

Student answer .... doesn't get the mark because ....

....

b) Now re-read the two answers that you decided were worth a mark. Which of them is the better answer? Justify your choice.

Student answer .... is the better answer because ....

....

Activity 4: Photographs

1. Study Figure 6 and then look at the question.

Figure 6 Aerial images of Las Vegas in 1973 (top) and 2010 (right)

Describe the growth of Las Vegas between 1973 and 2010. (2)

Now look at the following student answers. For each answer:

- highlight in green a very good, valid point definitely worth a mark
- highlight in pink a decent point probably worth a mark but not perfect
- highlight in yellow any comment/point that you think is irrelevant or an unnecessary repetition
- decide how many marks you should give each student answer.

Student answers		Mark
A	Las Vegas has grown a great deal. Some of the growth has been to the north-west.	
B	Las Vegas has exploded in every direction. This is because of the tourists.	
C	There are many reasons for the growth of Las Vegas. It has grown in many different ways.	
D	Las Vegas has grown by about 5 times. That growth is especially to the west and the south.	

2. Study Figure 7 and then look at the question.

Describe the changes in the sea-ice over the five weeks. (2)

Now look at the following student answer which scores 1 mark.

There is much less frozen sea-ice.

Which **two** of the following sentences would make this a full mark answer? Tick your choice.

A This is because of higher global warming. ☐

B The ice has retreated more than 50 km to the west. ☐

C There are now many more icebergs. ☐

D There is more ice visible everywhere. ☐

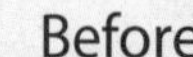

Before

After

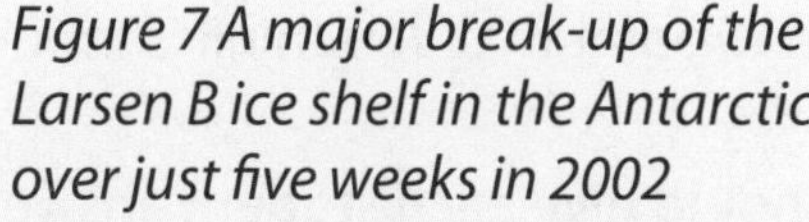
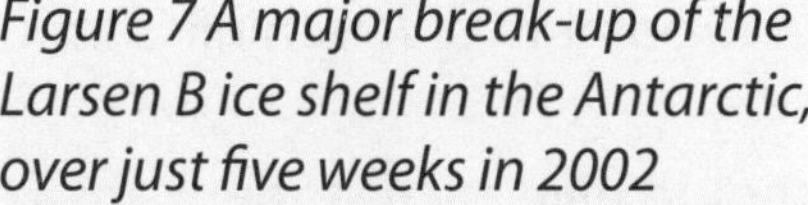

Figure 7 A major break-up of the Larsen B ice shelf in the Antarctic, over just five weeks in 2002

3. Study Figure 8 and then look at the question below.

Figure 8 Swanage beach and cliffs

Describe the cliff below the Grand Hotel. (3)

Look at the two student answers and choose the better one. Give a reason why.

Student answers	
A	The cliff is covered in vegetation and isn't completely steep. It has a wall at the bottom and some buildings as well.
B	The cliff is maybe 15 metres high and only about 70 degrees. There is a sea wall at the bottom to stop the cliff being eroded.

Student answer .... is better because...

....

Activity 5: Tables and graphs

1. Study Figure 9 and then look at the question below.

   Describe the changes in population shown. (2)

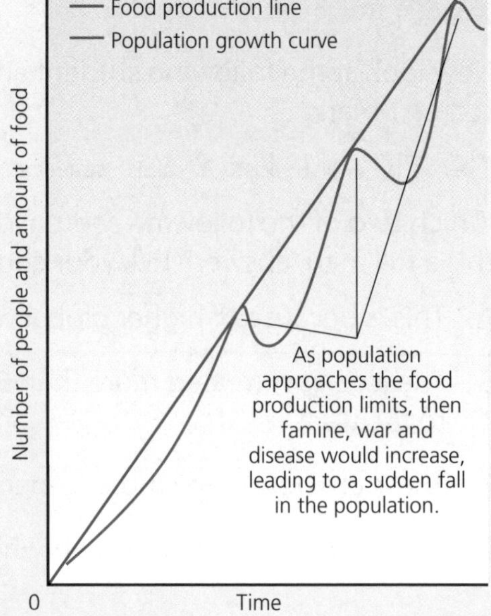

Figure 9 The relationship between food supply and population, according to Malthus

Now look at the following student answers. For each answer:

- highlight in green a very good, valid point definitely worth a mark
- highlight in pink a decent point probably worth a mark but not perfect
- highlight in yellow any comment/point that you think is irrelevant or an unnecessary repetition
- decide how many marks you should give each student answer.

Student answers		Mark
A	The population goes up most of the time. It sometimes doesn't when it hits the line.	
B	Population rises until it meets the resource line. It does go down sometimes quite regularly.	
C	Population falls because they run out of resources. Food production just keeps on rising.	
D	Food production rises as well as population. Then population falls quickly when it hits the resource line.	

2. a) Study Figure 10 and then look at the question below.

   Outline the differences between the population structure of Worthing and that of the UK. (2)

   Now look at the following student answer.

   The population of Worthing is different from that of London. ① It has fewer people between 15 and 24. ② There aren't many old people in the UK. ③

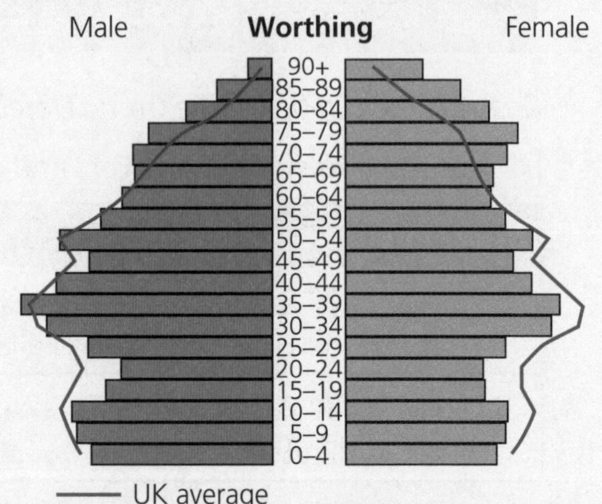

Figure 10 Population pyramid for Worthing, with the UK average shape superimposed

There are three sentences in this answer. Put them in order of usefulness with 1 = most useful to 3 = least useful. Complete the table.

Sentence	Order of usefulness
1	
2	
3	

b) Choose one of the sentences below to replace the weakest sentence and briefly explain the reason for your choice.

A Worthing has lost young people because of lack of work.

B Worthing has more old people, especially women.

I would replace the weakest sentence with sentence .... because ....

....

3. a) Study Figure 11 and then answer the question below.

Year	1800	1820	1840	1860	1880	1900	1920	1940	1960	1980	2008
Carbon dioxide (parts per million)	280	282	283	287	291	295	299	310	323	347	386
Methane (parts per million)	700	713	727	756	796	835	871	980	1430	1656	1940
Nitrous oxide (parts per million)	270	271	275	276	283	286	290	294	304	311	318

Figure 11 An estimate of the rise of the three main greenhouse gases

Identify the greenhouse gas that has increased most since 1800. (1)

Answer ....

b) Now look at this question and the following student answer.

Describe the changes in CO_2 between 1800 and 2008. (2)

Carbon dioxide had increased a lot. It started at 280 and has finished at 386.

This answer is worth 1 mark. Look at the student answers below.

- Highlight in green two answers that would add a mark
- Highlight in yellow the answer which is irrelevant because it doesn't follow the command word
- Highlight in blue the answer that is irrelevant because it doesn't recognise the focus of the question.

Student answers	
A	Other gases have increased by more.
B	It increased fastest from 1940.
C	This is because of human activity such as burning fossil fuels.
D	After a slow start the emissions have increased rapidly in recent years.

Unit 1 Dynamic planet

Section A

Topic 1 Restless Earth

This topic is divided into two parts:

- the first part is about the structure of the Earth
- the second part is about different types of plate boundaries and their different tectonic hazards.

Remember

In some cases you will gain marks for adding extra detail to a basic point. Sometimes you'll be asked to give details of a particular area such as a country or topic. You will have learnt examples for these in your GCSE course. Use fact sheets to make sure you know your facts and to build your knowledge.

Activity 1: Fact sheet

Complete the fact sheet below to build up some comparative examples of plate boundaries.

Contrasting plate boundaries: constructive vs destructive

	Constructive	Destructive
Example country / region		
Name and year of event		
Volcano type		
Magma type		
Explosivity		

Activity 2: Key terms

There are a number of key terms and definitions that you need to know to be confident in this section. The following will help you practise these. Circle the correct answer to each of these questions.

1. Constructive plate boundaries are where plates are moving in which direction in relation to each other?
   towards **away** **parallel**
2. What is the term for when an oceanic plate moves underneath continental plate at a zone of collision?
   denudation **subduction** **conflict**
3. What does the VEI (Volcanic Explosivity Index) measure?
   destructive power **height of ejected magma** **volcano age**
4. Why do lava flows rarely kill people?
   they are not very hot **generally very small** **they move slowly**
5. When a volcano is predicted, what do the authorities tend to tell people to do?
   hide under a table **go upstairs at home** **evacuate the area**

Activity 3: Understanding the exam question

1. Read the two example questions below and then look at the marks for each question.

   Example 1 *Give two characteristics of oceanic crust. (2)*

   Example 2 *Outline two ways in which buildings can be made more resistant to earthquakes. (2)*
   How much would you expect to write in your answer?
   Circle your choice.
   - Two sentences
   - A paragraph
   - Two or three paragraphs

2. How long do you think you should spend answering this type of question?
   Circle your choice.
   - Less than 1 minute
   - 2–3 minutes
   - 4–5 minutes

3. For the two questions above:
   a) underline the command word
   b) highlight key words such as technical language or important parts of the question to include in your answer.

4. Now decide what type of question it is. You must choose from: **description**, **example**, **assess**, or **explain**.

   Example 1 is a(n) .... question.

   This means ....

   Example 2 is a(n) .... question.

   This means ....

Activity 4: 2-mark questions

Hint
Look at the mark scheme on page 8 and remind yourself how you get marks for a 2-mark question.

Remember
Remember, that to get two marks you either need to
(a) give two separate clear ideas OR
(b) develop one reason more fully, perhaps giving more depth of detail.
How you get those two marks will depend on the style and nature of the question.

Identify why the following student answers do **not** get **2** marks for the question below. At the moment they get 1 mark.

Suggest one reason why the number of earthquake deaths varies in different countries. (2)

A: Some earthquakes kill more people because some earthquakes are bigger than others.

This answer would **not** get 2 marks because ....

B: In developing countries like Pakistan, they don't have emergency services that help people.

This answer would **not** get 2 marks because ....

Activity 5: 2-mark questions

Look at the student answers for each question below. For each answer:

- highlight in green a brief point
- highlight in blue support for a brief point
- highlight in yellow any comment/point that you think is irrelevant or an unnecessary repetition
- decide how many marks you should give each student answer.

1. *Describe the features of a shield volcano. (2)*

	Student answers	Mark
A	They are generally not very violent as they are not very tall.	
B	They are often shaped as a cone and release lava very slowly.	
C	Shield volcanoes are found at destructive plate boundaries and are highly explosive. There is a gradual build-up of runny lava.	
D	There is a steady accumulation of lava resulting in the flattish shape which can be very large in size.	

2. *Describe one way a region affected by earthquakes can prepare for this hazard. (2)*

	Student answers	Mark
A	They can hide under a table.	
B	People can build earthquake resistant buildings and houses which are shake-proof.	
C	Governments can get better systems to help people after an earthquake.	
D	Authorities can produce action plans. These tell the emergency services what to do in the event of an earthquake.	

Activity 6: 4-mark questions

Hint

Look at the mark scheme on page 9 and remind yourself about what you need to think about when writing a 4-mark answer.

Look at the student answers for the following question. For each answer:

- highlight in green a brief point
- highlight in blue support of a brief point
- highlight in yellow any comment/point that you think is irrelevant or an unnecessary repetition
- decide how many marks you should give each student answer.

Remember

You will need to develop ideas more fully for a 4-mark answer, spending probably 4–5 minutes answering it. You should write about a paragraph, somewhere in the region of 7–8 lines. A 4-mark question is still point marked. This means that you will get credit for each correct point that you make. You may also want to support your ideas with one or two examples, e.g. the names of regions or countries. Points can also be developed or extended for additional marks.

For either an earthquake or volcanic eruption you have studied, describe the immediate responses in managing its impact. (4)

	Student answers	Mark
A	In the earthquake in 2008 many people were killed as the quake occurred during the rush hour. Medical services tried to reach the area, however bridges that were needed had been destroyed.	
B	In Kobe, Japan, in 1995 a huge earthquake occurred. The immediate responses were to get emergency services out as swiftly as possible, to turn off all the gas in the area (preventing more fires and explosions in buildings) and to get medical care to the wounded. People were then given food and water and were relocated to refugee camps, as many homes were destroyed.	
C	In Japan there was an earthquake, people were evacuated and emergency services were prepared to help people. However, the impact of the volcano was as much as other volcanoes. The government issued appeals asking for help from other countries. Schools and public services were closed and insurance companies notified.	

Activity 7: 4-mark questions

1. Read the student answers to the following 4-mark questions and try to improve them.

Remember

Better answers are not necessarily longer answers but they are always more focused on the question. Key advice – keep them relevant and focused with no extra 'fluff'!

Describe two hazards volcanic eruptions can create for people. (4)

Extremely hot pyroclastic flows travel very quickly and can burn/scorch crops, woodland and kill wildlife in the area.

This answer would currently get 1 mark. Which **two** of the following sentences **together** would make it into a full mark answer? Tick your choices.

A Toxic gases such as sulphur from volcanoes cause breathing difficulties for people and health damage. ☐

B Landslides and volcanic mudslides can be triggered by volcanoes. ☐

C Volcanic mudslides can damage property and cause injury to people inside their houses. ☐

D A volcano such as Sakurajima (Japan) is on a destructive plate boundary; Japan has 10% of the world's active volcanoes. ☐

2. Now look at this student answer for the same question.

In some countries volcanoes can go off at any time and are therefore difficult to predict, like Mount St Helens. ① One immediate hazard is landslides which can damage property, block roads and even kill people. ② Ash can fall and build-up on the roofs of buildings causing them to sometimes collapse. ③

a) There are three sentences in this answer. Identify the weakest sentence and give your reason.

Sentence .... is the weakest because ....

....

b) Choose one of the two sentences below to replace the weakest sentence. Tick your choice.

A Volcanic hazards can impact on people and/or a region's / country's economy. ☐

B Volcanic hazards are generally limited to physical impacts, e.g. causing deaths. ☐

3. The following student answer would currently get 2 marks for this 4-mark question.

Explain why earthquakes happen on destructive plate margins. (4)

Destructive plate boundaries are where plates are moving together, e.g. Pacific and Philippine plates. These are sometimes called conflict boundaries.

Which **two** sentences **together** would most help raise this to a full mark answer? Tick your choices.

A In the Pacific Ring of Fire earthquakes are common. ☐

B There is pressure at the plate boundary sometimes associated with earthquakes. ☐

C Subduction zones are stores of pressure which are suddenly released. ☐

D Earthquakes are a form of energy release which occur when there is a build up of pressure. ☐

4. There are three sentences in this student answer. Put them in order of usefulness with 1 = most useful to 3 = least useful. Give a reason why you have put them in this order.

Earthquakes occur when there is a release of pressure at a point where two plates are coming together. ① Destructive margins are plates where two plates are next to each other. ② Earthquakes are found at these margins because stored energy is released during the movement of plates. ③

Sentence	Order of usefulness	Reason
1		
2		
3		

Topic 2 Climate and change

This topic is divided into two parts:

- the first part is about how climate has changed in the past
- the second part is about how a changing climate might present future difficulties or challenges for people.

Remember

In some cases you will gain marks for adding extra detail to a basic point. Sometimes you'll be asked to give details of a particular area such as a country or topic. You will have learnt examples for these in your GCSE course. Use fact sheets to make sure you know your facts and to build your knowledge.

Activity 1: Fact sheets

1. Complete the fact sheet below to build up a brief example of how **one selected** country from the developing world will probably be affected by climate change.

Climate change – developing country example

Chosen country ....

Social impacts ....

....

Economic impacts ....

....

Environmental impacts ....

....

2. Complete the table below to list some of the likely natural and human causes of climate change.

Natural causes of climate change	Human causes of climate change

Activity 2: Key terms

There are a number of key terms and definitions that you need to know to be confident in this section. The following will help you practise these. Circle the correct answer to each of these questions.

1. Which **two** of the following are thought to be a natural cause of climate change?
   sun-spot cycles **volcanoes** **deforestation**
2. Which of the following developing countries will be worst affected by sea-level rise as a result of climate change?
   Banglasdesh **Greece** **Nepal**
3. Which of the following human activities is **not** a major source of greenhouse gases?
   intensive farming **smoking** **air travel**

Activity 3: Understanding the exam question

1. Read the two example questions below and then look at the marks for each question.
   Example 1 *What is the enhanced greenhouse effect? (2)*
   Example 2 *Outline one possible human cause of climate change. (2)*
   How much would you expect to write in your answer? Circle your choice.
   - Two sentences
   - A paragraph
   - Two or three paragraphs
2. How long do you think you should spend answering this question? Circle your choice.
   - Less than 1 minute
   - 2–3 minutes
   - 4–5 minutes
3. For the two questions above:
   a) underline the command word
   b) highlight key words such as technical language or important parts of the question to include in your answer.
4. Now decide what type of question it is. You must choose from: **description**, **example**, **assess**, or **explain**.

   Example 1 is a(n) .... question. This means ....

   ....

   Example 2 is a(n) .... question. This means..............................

   ....

Activity 4: 2-mark questions

Hint

Look at the mark scheme on page 8 and remind yourself how you get marks for a 2-mark question.

Remember

To get two marks you either need to:

(i) give two separate clear ideas OR

(ii) develop one reason more fully, perhaps giving more depth of detail.

How you get those two marks will depend on the style and nature of the question.

Identify why the following student answers do **not** get 2 marks for the question.
At the moment they get 1 mark.

*Give **two** reasons why developing countries often produce less carbon dioxide than developed countries. (2)*

A: They trade less with other countries and they have weaker economies than MEDCs.

This answer would not get 2 marks because ....

....

B: They have better ways of reducing their emissions, e.g. better pollution law.

This answer would not get 2 marks because ....

....

Activity 5: 2-mark questions

Look at the student answers for each question below. For each answer:

- highlight in green a brief point
- highlight in blue support for a brief point
- highlight in yellow any comment/point that you think is irrelevant or an unnecessary repetition
- decide how many marks you should give each student answer.

1. *Describe how colder periods, such as the Little Ice Age, affected farming. (2)*

Student answers		Mark
A	People were able to grow less food due to all the rain.	
B	Agricultural productivity was changed as a result of the Little Ice Age.	
C	Cold periods mean you can grow less plants so there are less crops.	
D	Crops were frozen and there were the Thames Frost Fairs.	

2. *Describe **one** natural cause of climate change. (2)*

Student answers		Mark
A	Sometimes emissions from volcanoes can cause problems for people.	
B	Carbon dioxide from power stations is a cause of climate change.	
C	Sun-spot cycles cause changes in the Earth's temperature.	
D	The distance the Earth is away from the Sun can vary over long periods of time.	

Activity 6: 4-mark questions

Hint

Look at the mark scheme on page 9 and remind yourself about what you need to think about for writing a 4-mark answer.

Remember

You will need to develop ideas more fully for a 4-mark answer, spending probably 4–5 minutes answering it. You should write about a paragraph, somewhere in the region of 7–8 lines. A 4-mark question is still point marked. This means that you will get credit for each correct point that you make. You may also want to support your ideas with one or two examples, e.g. the names of regions or countries. Points can also be developed or extended for additional marks.

Look at the student answers for each of the following question. For each answer:

- highlight in green a brief point
- highlight in blue support for a brief point
- highlight in yellow any comment/point that you think is irrelevant or an unnecessary repetition
- decide how many marks you should give each student answer.

*For a **named developing country**, explain why climate change is likely to have a large impact on its people. (4)*

	Student answers	Mark
A	Example: the UK. Ski resorts in Scotland could be affected with less days of snow damaging the economy. Also there may be an increase in beach tourism, e.g. in Cornwall which would be a good effect for local businesses, e.g. hotels and surf-schools.	
B	In Bangladesh climate change is going to mean the country floods a lot more. As ice melts more water will end up in the sea. People will have to move from their homes as river levels rise. The ground will become infiltrated and they won't be able to grow crops.	
C	Wildlife and plants will die as a result of climate change; although others may appear as they like the changed climate. My example country is Ethiopia. People do not have the knowledge to cope with a lack of water so dehydration would be a real problem. They can't afford to build reservoirs to combat the droughts from climate change.	

Activity 7: 4-mark questions

1. Read the student answers to the following 4-mark questions and try to improve them.

   Explain the possible economic impacts of climate change on a named country. (4)

   In the UK climate change could lead to long-term crop damage and a loss of agricultural output.

Remember

Better answers are not necessarily longer answers but they are always more focused on the question. Key advice – keep them relevant and focused with no extra 'fluff'!

This answer would currently get 2 marks. Which **two** of the following sentences **together** would make this into a full mark answer? Tick your choices.

A It could also lead to more river flooding. ☐

B In Bangladesh there will be more coastal flooding. ☐

C Economic effects of climate change would cost the government more money. ☐

D Increased river flooding causes damage to houses and businesses which is an economic effect. ☐

2. Now look at this student answer which is for the same question.

In some countries climate change will have a big economic impact. ① In Spain there is likely be a reduction in river levels used for getting drinking water. ② Therefore more money will be needed to supply drinking water from alternative means, e.g. reservoirs, especially for tourists in the summer. ③

a) There are three sentences in this answer. Identify the weakest sentence and explain your choice.

Sentence .... is the weakest because ....

....

b) Choose **one** of the two sentences below to replace the weakest sentence. Tick your choice.

A Spain is in the Mediterranean and will suffer economically from climate change; there are going to be many effects including drought. ☐

B Spain will find that there may be an increased burden on its hospitals as people get more dehydrated in the hotter summers. ☐

3. The following student answer would currently get 2 marks for this 4-mark question.

*Describe **two** natural causes of climate change. (4)*

Emissions from volcanoes can lead to dust in the atmosphere blocking out the incoming solar radiation.

Which **two** sentences **together** would most help raise this to a full mark answer? Tick your choices.

A The solar activity from the Sun varies over long periods of time affecting the climate on the Earth. ☐

B The amount of ice at the poles reflects solar radiation that could affect how hot the Earth is. ☐

C Increasing emission of gases like sulphur dioxide from natural volcanoes leads to the greenhouse effect. ☐

D Climate change is also caused by combustion of fossil fuels which is a natural process. ☐

Topic 3 Battle for the biosphere

This topic is divided into two parts:

- the first part is about the importance and distribution of different biomes
- the second part is about how people may be altering the biosphere and how these effects can be managed.

Remember

In some cases you will gain marks for adding extra detail to a basic point. Sometimes you'll be asked to give details of a particular area such as a country or topic. You will have learnt examples for these in your GCSE course. Use the fact sheets like the one below to make sure you know your facts and build your knowledge.

Activity 1: Fact sheets

Complete the fact sheet below to build up an example of **one biome**, e.g. tropical rainforest or coral reefs, the goods and services it provides and conservation strategies.

1 Goods and services

Chosen biome/large-scale ecosystem ....

Description ....

....

List of services ....

....

List of goods ....

....

2 Conservation strategies

Local	Global
Named example (place):	Named example (place):
Players / organisations:	Players / organisations:
Example strategies:	Example strategies:

Activity 2: Key terms

There are a number of key terms and definitions that you need to know to be confident in this section. The following will help you practise these. Circle the correct answer to each of these questions.

1. A woodland ecosystem supplies fuel wood. What is this an example of?

   energy **a good** **a service**

2. Which of the following is not an example of a global framework for biodiversity management?

   Greenpeace **RAMSAR** **CITES**

3. Eco-tourism should represent an example of what type of approach to longer-term resource management?

   extractive **exploitative** **sustainable**

Activity 3: Understanding the exam question

1. Look at the two example questions below and then look at the marks for each question.

   Example 1 *Give **two** examples of **either** goods or services from an ecosystem. (2)*

   Example 2 *Outline **one** way that some environments are threatened. (2)*

   How much would you expect to write in your answer? Circle your choice.

   - Two sentences
   - A paragraph
   - Two or three paragraphs

2. How long do you think you should spend answering this question? Circle your choice.
   - Less than 1 minute
   - 2–3 minutes
   - 4–5 minutes

3. For the two questions above:

   a) underline the command word

   b) highlight key words such as technical language or important parts of the question to include in your answer.

4. Now decide what type of question it is. You must choose from: **description**, **example**, **assess**, or **explain**.

   Example 1 is a(n) .... question. This means ....

   ....

   Example 2 is a(n) .... question. This means..

   ....

Activity 4: 2-mark questions

Hint

Look at the mark scheme on page 8 and remind yourself how you get marks for a 2-mark question.

Remember

To get two marks you either need to:

(i) give two separate clear ideas OR

(ii) develop one reason more fully, perhaps giving more depth of detail.

How you get those two marks will depend on the style and nature of the question.

1. Identify why the following student answers do **not** get **2** marks for this question. At the moment they get 1 mark.

   Briefly suggest ***two*** *reasons why in some parts of the world tropical rainforest is being cut down (deforestation). (2)*

   A: Because people need to use the wood to burn for heat and cooking.

   This answer would not get two marks because ....

   ....

   B: The timber is valuable (exports) and it is also cheap and easy to chop.

   This answer would not get 2 marks because ....

   ....

Activity 5: 2-mark questions

Look at the student answers for each question below. For each answer:

- highlight in green a brief point
- highlight in blue support for a brief point
- highlight in yellow any comment/point that you think is irrelevant or an unnecessary repetition
- decide how many marks you should give each student answer.

1. *Describe* ***one*** *way of conserving threatened environments. (2)*

Student answers		Mark
A	You could develop a park which might help save some important plant species; you can also stop people treading on the plants too because of footpath erosion.	
B	Ban all hunting of the area, this may make local people hungry or cause them to go without clothing.	
C	Set up trade agreements, e.g. CITES to ban the sale or export of things from protected species like ivory from elephants..	
D	Promote eco-tourism, in places like Africa, where people pay to kill animals as trophies.	

2. *Describe* ***one*** *effect of deforestation on the environment. (2)*

Student answers		Mark
A	There is a loss of income for local people once forests are cut down (no more forest goods).	
B	Causes climate change by changing the reflectivity of a surface (albedo).	
C	Removal of the trees lowers the quality of the soil (nutrients); trees also protect the soil from harsh weather.	
D	Trees are a cash crop. Their sale as an export generates money for the country, e.g. Brazil. So too many being cut down has a big effect.	

Activity 6: 4-mark questions

Hint

Look at the mark scheme on page 9 and remind yourself about what you need to think about for writing a 4-mark answer.

Remember

You will need to develop ideas more fully for a 4-mark answer, spending probably 4–5 minutes answering it. You should write about a paragraph, somewhere in the region of 7–8 lines. A 4-mark question is still point marked. This means that you will get credit for each correct point that you make. You may also want to support your ideas with one or two examples, e.g. the names of regions or countries. Points can also be developed or extended for additional marks.

Look at the student answers for the following question. For each answer:

- highlight in green a brief point
- highlight in blue support for a brief point
- highlight in yellow any comment/point that you think is irrelevant or an unnecessary repetition
- decide how many marks you should give each student answer.

*For **one** biome, outline some of goods and services that it provides. (4)*

	Student answers	Mark
A	The rainforest provides us with many goods and services including air to breathe and timber for making furniture. Other biomes also provide things.	
B	Rainforests provide a number of goods such as medicines for people (genetic diversity), lots of different types of food like berries and also raw materials, e.g. timber for construction. We all need goods and services as they are important.	
C	Goods include things that people use directly such as food from seas or medicines from the rainforest. Services on the other hand involves things like regulation, e.g. to do with water resources or in the development of different types of soil.	

Activity 7: 4-mark questions

Remember

Better answers are not necessarily longer answers but they are always more focused on the question. Key advice – keep them relevant and focused with no extra 'fluff'!

1. Read the student answers to the following 4-mark questions and try to improve them.

   Examine the factors that can control the distribution of one type of ecosystem or biome. (4)

   The most important factor is usually climate; the amount of rainfall and the annual temperature range/number of days growing season.

   This answer would currently get 2 marks. Which **two** of the following sentences **individually** would make this into a full 4-mark answer? Tick your choices.

   A How dry the area is, is important, and whether or not the ecosystem is close to the sea. ☐

   B Other factors (perhaps locally very important) could include altitude and the impact of people, e.g. removal of trees for farming. ☐

C The impact of people using the biome, e.g. people diving on coral reef resources has an impact on the distribution. ☐

D Soil type and geology may also be important as could the seasonality of precipitation during the year. ☐

2. Now look at this student answer which is for the same question.

For all biomes climate (rainfall, temperature, length of growing season, etc) is a very important factor influencing distribution. ① The height of the biome may also be something to think about, although it may not be important. ② Where biomes are found is also controlled by where they were originally planted by people. ③

a) There are three sentences in this answer. Identify the weakest sentence and give your reason.

Sentence .... is the weakest because ....

....

b) Choose one of the two sentences below to replace the weakest sentence. Tick your choice.

A Other local factors such as the effects of management by people or the distance from the sea could be significant. ☐

B In some places biomes are protected by conservation to maintain their original state. ☐

3. The following student answer would currently get 2 marks for this 4-mark question.

Using examples, describe how some places are using a number of conservation strategies. (4)

In the UK, National Parks are a way of protecting the landscape and conserve natural biodiversity. Sustainable management is also important, for example in Cameroon there is a sustainable forest reserve called Kilum.

Which **two** sentences **together** would help raise this to a full mark answer? Tick your choices.

A The reserve has a mix of core conservation areas and buffer zones. ☐

B In parts of southern Africa people can make money from game hunting. ☐

C Also sustainable development may involve community involvement. ☐

D The land is also divided into different areas such as eco-tourism, agroforestry and selective logging areas. ☐

4. There are three sentences in this answer. Put them in order of usefulness with 1 = most useful to 3 = least useful. Give a reason why you have put them in this order.

Conservation strategies are used to help conserve landscapes and ecosystems. ① Community forests have been used in England to provide new areas of woodland close to major cities like Manchester. ② International treaties such as RAMSAR have been important in protecting important wetlands in some places. ③

Sentence	Order of usefulness	Reason
1		
2		
3		

Topic 4 Water world

This topic is divided into two parts:

- the first part is about the importance of the hydrological cycle to the planets regulation
- the second part is concerned with the sustainable management of water resources.

Remember

In some cases you will gain marks for adding extra detail to a basic point. Sometimes you'll be asked to give details of a particular area such as a country or topic. You will have learnt examples for these in your GCSE course. Use the fact sheets like the one below to make sure you know your facts and build your knowledge.

Activity 1: Fact sheets

Complete the fact sheet below to build up a short case study of how over use of water has led to a reduction in the **amount** of water available for people (drinking supplies).

Reduction in amount of water

Chosen country .... region/area ....

List three reasons why there was a **reduction in the amount** of water:

1. ....

2. ....

3. ....

What are the possible solutions/management strategies?

1. ....

2. ....

Complete the fact sheet below to build up a short case study of how over use of water has led to a reduction in water **quality**.

Reduction in water quality

Chosen country .... region/area ....

List three reasons why there was a **reduction in the water quality**:

1. ....

2. ....

3. ....

What are the possible solutions/management strategies?

1. ....

2. ....

Activity 2: Key terms

There are a number of key terms and definitions that you need to know to be confident in this section. The following will help you practise these. Circle the correct answer to each of these questions.

1. Which of the three terms is **not** associated with the hydrological cycle?

   salinisation **evaporation** **condensation**

2. Taking water from rivers and aquifers for use as a drinking water source is called?

   pumping **abstraction** **potable**

3. What type of technology is rainwater harvesting?

   appropriate **exploitative** **high**

Activity 3: Understanding the exam question

1. Read the two example questions below and then look at the marks for each question.

   Example 1 *Suggest* ***two*** *benefits of large-scale water projects such as dam construction. (2)*

   Example 2 *Outline* ***one*** *way in which water can move between stores in the hydrological cycle. (2)*

   How much would you expect to write in your answer? Circle your choice.

   - Two sentences
   - A paragraph
   - Two or three paragraphs

2. How long do you think you should spend answering this type of question? Circle your choice.

   - Less than 1 minute
   - 2–3 minutes
   - 4–5 minutes

3. For the two questions above:

   a) underline the command word

   b) highlight key words such as technical language or important parts of the question to include in your answer.

4. Now decide what type of question it is. You must choose from: **description**, **example**, **assess**, or **explain**.

   Example 1 is a(n) .... question. This means ....

   ....

   Example 2 is a(n) .... question. This means..

   ....

Activity 4: 2-mark questions

Hint
Look at the mark scheme on page 8 and remind yourself how you get marks for a 2-mark question.

Remember
To get two marks you either need to:
(i) give two separate clear ideas OR
(ii) develop one reason more fully, perhaps giving more depth of detail.
How you get those two marks will depend on the style and nature of the question.

Identify why the following student answers do **not** get **2** marks for the question.
At the moment they get 1 mark.

Why is the hydrological cycle often described as a system? (2)

A: Because it is like a circle and things go round it always ending up in the sea or in lakes.

This answer would not get 2 marks because ....

....

B: It has inputs and outputs which are found in any system.

This answer would not get 2 marks because ....

....

Activity 5: 2-mark questions

Look at the student answers for each question below. For each answer:

- highlight in green a brief point
- highlight in blue support for a brief point
- highlight in yellow any comment/point that you think is irrelevant or an unnecessary repetition
- decide how many marks you should give each student answer.

1. *Describe how **one** human activity can result in a decline in water quality. (2)*

	Student answers	Mark
A	Boats emit wastes into the sea water making it dirty. This ends up on beaches.	
B	Toxic waste is often dumped into the sea making it impure and dangerous. This waste can come from power stations.	
C	Pollution of groundwater supplies can reduce water quality and hurt fish.	
D	Adding nitrate fertilisers, e.g. in East Anglia, can run off fields and end up in streams causing pollution.	

2. *Describe **one** impact of water shortages on people. (2)*

	Student answers	Mark
A	They do not have enough to drink and go thirsty. There is also the risk of ecosystems and habitats becoming damaged.	
D	Unreliable rainfall can make farming extremely difficult. Drought conditions can lead to crop failure and famine.	
C	Tensions over water supply can result in war in some places as people do not have enough to drink. This is what we call 'water wars' and will be a growing problem in the future, especially in Wales.	
D	Low water levels can affect fish in rivers which has an impact on people.	

Activity 6: 4-mark questions

Hint

Look at the mark scheme on page 9 and remind yourself about what you need to think about for writing a 4-mark answer.

Remember

You will need to develop ideas more fully for a 4-mark answer, spending probably 4–5 minutes answering it. You should write about a paragraph, somewhere in the region of 7–8 lines. A 4-mark question is still point marked. This means that you will get credit for each correct point that you make. You may also want to support your ideas with one or two examples, e.g. the names of regions or countries. Points can also be developed or extended for additional marks.

1. Look at the student answers for the following questions. For each answer:
   - highlight in green a brief point
   - highlight in blue support for a brief point
   - highlight in yellow any comment/point that you think is irrelevant or an unnecessary repetition
   - decide how many marks you should give each student answer.

   Using examples, explain how human activity can reduce water supplies. (4)

Student answers		Mark
A	Pollution from power stations causes increased pollution in the air which can get into rivers and lakes. Climate change is to blame for this which is caused by human activity. Also as the world is getting hotter there will be more evaporation from lakes which will mean less water is available for drinking supplies.	
B	Reduction in supply due to over-abstraction of groundwater, e.g. in Spanish 'Costas' is a big problem especially with a large number of summer visitors. They should reduce the amount of water available (i.e. only turn it on for certain times of the day), or make the water very expensive. This would mean that people would use less.	
C	Getting more and more water from rivers causes a lack of water downstream which can affect villages further along the river. This is happening in many parts of the world including where I live. The local water company is being blamed for taking too much water and letting the fish die as a result.	

Activity 7: 4-mark questions

Remember

Better answers are not necessarily longer answers but they are always more focused on the question. Key advice – keep them relevant and focused with no extra 'fluff'!

1. Read the student answers to the following 4-mark questions and try to improve them.

   *Describe the costs and **benefits** of a named large-scale water management project. (4)*

In the Three Gorges Dam (China) a lot of people lost their homes and were forcibly relocated as part of the multi-million pound scheme.

This answer would currently get 2 marks. Which **two** of the following sentences **individually** would make this a full 4-mark answer? Tick your choices.

A However, it did provide a safe drinking water supply and also lots of employment when it was being built. ☐

B There were a number of other disadvantages including the fact there was a lot of environmentally damaging concrete used during its construction; it was also very expensive. ☐

C The people who were displaced did find new homes and so were happy. ☐

D The large scale top-down project now produces lots of electricity for people and businesses. ☐

2. Now look at this student answer for the same question.

Dams built in the Colorado River trap silt and sand which makes it costly to initially build. ① The benefits are that it is a store of hydroelectric power which is a renewable source of energy. ② The dam was built to store water for future use. ③

a) There are three sentences in this answer. Identify the weakest sentence and give your reason.

Sentence .... is the weakest because ....

....

b) Choose one of the two sentences below to replace the weakest sentence. Tick your choice.

A The dam has significant environmental impacts as many people disagreed with it being built. ☐

B In some instances, however, the dam can stop the flow of water downstream which upsets other ecosystems. ☐

3. This answer would currently get 2 marks.

Using an example(s), explain why small scale solutions to managing water supplies are often sustainable. (4).

In the hand dug wells in Ethiopia all the materials used were local and the construction method made use of the skills and expertise of local people.

Which **two** sentences **individually** would most help raise this to a full mark answer? Tick your choices.

A As these wells were built by local people they were cheap to finance and many were dug by hand. ☐

B If there was a problem with the well in the future, in most circumstances local people could quickly fix the well; the technology used is low-cost and intermediate (so can be understood). ☐

C The cost of the wells was low and affordable, local people could expect to use these for a long time into the future. ☐

D They also had water pumps installed; these worked well and the local people could collect lots of water. ☐

Section B
Topic 5 Coastal change and conflict

This is the first option in Section B; you have either studied this option or Topic 6 River processes and pressures (see pages 45–50).

This topic is divided into two parts:

- the first part reveals how physical processes lead to different types of coast
- the second part is about coastal management, set against the backdrop of different interest groups or stakeholders.

Hint
There are no named locations that you must study but you are expected to have looked at the contrasts between a 'hard rock' and 'soft rock' coastline.

Remember
In some cases you will gain marks for adding extra detail to a basic point. Sometimes you'll be asked to give details of a particular area such as a country or topic. You will have learnt examples for these in your GCSE course. Use fact sheets to make sure you know your facts and build your knowledge.

Activity 1: Fact sheet

Complete the fact sheet below to build up two mini case studies.

Contrasting coastal areas boundaries: 'hard rock' vs 'soft rock'

	Hard rock	Soft rock
Example country /region		
Geology at location		
Erosional landforms		
Cliff type		
Depositional landforms		

Activity 2: Key terms

There are a number of key terms and definitions that you need to know to be confident in this section. The following will help you practise these. Circle the correct answer to each of these questions.

1. On coasts with hard resistant rocks, the rate of coastal erosion is…
   rapid **slow** **unusual**
2. The process of wearing away and breaking down rocks is called…
   erosion **deposition** **transportation**
3. What kind of coastline is it when rock structures / layers of rock are parallel to the coast?
   concordant **discordant** **peculiar**
4. The highest point on a wave is called the…
   trough **wavelength** **crest**
5. Spits are usually formed by the process of…
   hydraulic action **attrition** **longshore drift**

Activity 3: Understanding the exam question

1. Look at the two example questions below and then look at the marks for each question.

   Example 1 *Outline **one** process of coastal erosion. (2)*

   Example 2 *Give **brief** details as to how the process of longshore drift operates. (2)*

   How much would you expect to write in your answer? Circle your choice.

   - Two sentences
   - A paragraph
   - Two or three paragraphs

2. How long do you think you should spend answering this type of question? Circle your choice.

   - Less than 1 minute
   - 2–3 minutes
   - 4–5 minutes

3. For the two questions above:

   a) underline the command word

   b) highlight key words such as technical language or important parts of the question to include in your answer.

4. Now decide what type of question it is. You must choose from: **description**, **example**, **assess**, or **explain**.

   Example 1 is a(n) .... question. This means ....

   ....

   Example 2 is a(n) .... question. This means..

   ....

Activity 4: 2- or 3- mark questions

Hint

Look at the mark scheme on page 8 and remind yourself how you get marks for a 2- or 3-mark question.

Identify why the following student answers do **not** get **3** marks for the question. At the moment they get 2 marks.

Suggest how physical processes can cause coastal problems and threats to people. (3)

Remember

To get two marks you either need to:

(a) give two/three separate clear ideas OR

(b) develop one or two reason(s) more fully, perhaps giving more depth of detail.

How you get those two marks will depend on the style and nature of the question.

A: Physical processes can be things like erosion, e.g. at the Holderness coast. Erosion causes cliff collapse and loss of land.

This answer would not get 3 marks because ....

....

B: Loss of agricultural land and land for housing is a big problem where there is rapid coastal erosion.

This answer would not get 3 marks because ....

....

Activity 5: 2- or 3-mark questions

Look at the student answers for each question below. For each answer:

- highlight in green a brief point
- highlight in blue support for a brief point
- highlight in yellow any comment/point that you think is irrelevant or an unnecessary repetition
- decide how many marks you should give each student answer.

1. *Name and describe one process of coastal erosion. (2)*

	Student answers	Mark
A	Longshore drift is a process whereby sand and stones are moved along the beach. The process is controlled by the influence of the direction of the prevailing wind.	
B	Stacks are formed at the coast (often hard rocks). Erosion enlarges a geological weakness and eventually leads to the development of an arch, then a stack over a long period of time.	
C	Hydraulic action works by the compression of air in cracks in rocks. It can lead to the development of the headland-arch-stack-stump sequence.	
D	Loose rocks are thrown against the cliffs by waves. This wears away the cliff surface and bits of eroded rock can then fall off the cliff.	

2. *Describe the process of longshore drift. (3)*

	Student answers	Mark
A	Longshore drift describes movement of material along a beach. Waves hit the beach at an angle and push up material, then the material is deposited.	
B	Longshore drift is when waves crash at the shore at an angle. The waves carry sediment which builds up to form a spit.	
C	A process where rocks and other materials are moved by the backwash of the sea and then deposited further down shore. Longshore drift can cause serious problems for fishermen by trapping sand in their nets.	
D	A spit is the result of longshore drift caused by constructive waves. This means the wave's backwash has more force than swash and pulls sediment away from the beach. It gets deposited further along the beach.	

Activity 6: 6-mark questions

Hint

Look at the mark scheme on page 10 and remind yourself how you get marks for a 6-mark question. Think about 'building an answer' rather than just telling a case-study type story.

Remember

Remember that you will need to develop ideas more fully for a 6-mark answer, spending probably 7–8 minutes answering it. You would be expected to write perhaps two paragraphs, somewhere in the region of 8–10 lines. Remember, a 6-mark question will be marked on three levels. These levels describe the general quality of the work. For this more extended writing you will also be assessed on the quality of written communication. This is identified by *. Please see page 10 for more information on levels.

*****_For **two** different types of sea defences, explain how they reduce erosion. (6)_

Read the following student answers to the question above. You are going to try and improve them.

Student answers	
A	Defence 1: Rip rap can be made of a range of hard rock types including granite and limestone. Defence 2: Gabions are cages of rocks that can be placed at the base of cliffs to reduce wave energy.
B	Defence 1: Sea wall – this reduces wave energy. It also settles the water down and can prevent access to the beach (steps needed). The bullnose shape throws waves up and back out to sea. Defence 2: Groynes work by trying to prevent longshore drift by operating as a physical barrier. These have been installed at many parts of the coast, including North Norfolk, to try and reduce coastal erosion.

1. Student answer A is falling short of full marks – only getting 1 or 2 marks. We need to add an extra sentence to 'Defence 1' and 'Defence 2' to get maximum marks (3 + 3) as the question asks for two types of sea defence. There are two pairs of sentences below for Defence 1 and Defence 2. Tick your choice of sentences to ensure top marks and then explain why.

   A Defence 1 – Soft engineering such as beach re-grading works by reducing the wave energy as it approaches the coastline; it is very effective. ☐

   B Defence 1 – Rip-rap works by absorbing and deflecting the impact of a wave before the wave reaches the defended structure, e.g. a sea wall. ☐

   C Defence 2 – They work by absorbing the impact of large waves before they can begin to erode the base of a cliff. ☐

   D Defence 2 – Gabions have the advantage that they are easily constructed and can act effectively as a cheap sea wall. ☐

   For Defence 1 I chose sentence .... because ....

   ....

   For Defence 2 I chose sentence .... because ....

   ....

2 Student answer B:

   a) Identify the stronger and weakest sentences for each defence. Highlight the stronger sentence in blue and the weakest in green.

   b) Now write a new sentence to replace each weak sentence.

   Defence 1 ....

   Defence 2 ....

Activity 7: 6-mark questions

1. Look at the student answers for the question below. For each answer:
   - highlight in green a brief point
   - highlight in blue support for a brief point
   - highlight in yellow any comment/point that you think is irrelevant or an unnecessary repetition
   - decide how many marks you should give each student answer and why.

**For a named location, explain the costs and benefits of using hard engineering techniques to protect a coastline from erosion. (6)*

	Student answers	Mark	Reason
A	Swanage Bay has many of the problems of coastal erosion. Over the years it has obviously formed a bay. It gets a lot of destructive waves that damage the coastline. The sea wall is there to try and protect the coastline. It lasts for about 30–50 years. Rock armour is very good at protecting the coast. Soft engineering may be cheaper and can include cliff-face vegetation and beach nourishment.		
B	At Hornsea hard engineering has been put in place in the form of groynes, rip-rap and a sea wall. One benefit has been that it retains the town's popular beach and also protects the town from the giant waves due to the huge fetch that comes in from the North Sea. This can lead to large waves and storm surges in the winter months. However, groynes look ugly and can deter visitors. Also the groynes mentioned stop the process of longshore drift so the cliffs further down the coast are being eroded away as a result. Re-grading is another method, but tends to be associated with integrated coastal zone management.		
C	Revetments are used at Barton-on-Sea; these are an effective way of protecting the coastline and they look natural. However, they are expensive (approx. £2000 per metre) and must be repaired. Groynes are used to stop longshore drift and act as a good type of defence to help build up tourist beaches. Again, they are costly – about £10,000 each – and can lead to the sediment starvation further down the coast. Lastly, gabions are used to protect the cliff. These are pretty cheap at £300 per metre and absorb wave energy, but they don't last very long.		

2. Using the question above and ideas from these three responses, build your own A-A* answer that you think would get maximum marks on a separate piece of paper.

Remember

Use your own case study material that you developed at the beginning of this section on page 40. These answers require a little more use of case study material than you have previously done before. Try to use a few selected facts and figures to support your answer. This adds depth. Use of paragraphs is also a good idea.

Topic 6 River processes and pressures

This is the second option in Section B; you have either studied this option or Topic 5 Coastal change and conflict. (see pages 40–4).

This topic is divided into two parts:

- the first part reveals how physical processes lead to the development of river systems and landforms
- the second part is about river flooding and the options for management.

Remember

In some cases you will gain marks for adding extra detail to a basic point. Sometimes you'll be asked to give details of a particular area such as a country or topic. You will have learnt examples for these in your GCSE course. Use fact sheets to make sure you know your facts and build your knowledge.

Hint

There are no named locations that you must study but you are expected to have looked at the contrasts between a 'hard rock' and 'soft rock' coastline.

Activity 1: Fact sheets

Complete the fact sheet below to build up a flooding case study.

Flooding case study

	Details
Example country/ region/place	
Date of flood	
Causes of the flood/ background	
Description of flood impacts (magnitude, losses, etc)	
Options for the future/ lessons learnt	

Complete the fact sheet below which identifies river features: upper, middle and lower course, and the linked processes.

River features

	Features / landforms	Brief description of the dominant processes and characteristics
Upper		
Middle		
Lower		

Activity 2: Key terms

There are a number of key terms and definitions that you need to know to be confident in this section. The following will help you practise these.

embankments	flood relief channel	dams	levees

1. Fill in the hard-engineering type from the box above. Not all the words have to be used.
   a) Made of earth and grass it stops water spreading out on to the flood plain ....
   b) In the headwaters of a river system, large stores of water ....
   c) Like a bypass channel, taking water away from towns and cities ....

meander	ox-bow lake	waterfall	interlocking spurs	levee	floodplain

2. Fill in the landform type from the box above. Not all the words have to be used.
   a) Natural embankments of sediment along the side of a river ....
   b) Wide flat area of land in the lower course of a river ....
   c) Large bends in a river's course ....
   d) Promontories of hills jutting out into a river valley in a staggered formation ....

   ....

Activity 3: Understanding the exam question

1. Look at the two example questions below and then look at the marks for each question.

   Example 1 *Outline one process of river erosion. (2)*

   Example 2 *State what is meant by the term 'lag-time'. (2)*

   How much would you expect to write in your answer? Circle your choice.
   - Two sentences
   - A paragraph
   - Two or three paragraphs

2. How long do you think you should spend answering this question? Circle your choice.
   - Less than 1 minute
   - 2–3 minutes
   - 4–5 minutes

3. For the two questions above:
   a) underline the command word
   b) highlight key words such as technical language or important parts of the question to include in your answer.

4. Now decide what type of question it is. You must choose from: **description**, **example**, **definition**, or **explain**.

   Example 1 is a(n) .... question. This means ....

   ....

   Example 2 is a(n) .... question. This means..

   ....

Activity 4: 2- or 3- mark questions

Hint

Look at the mark scheme on page 8 and remind yourself how you get marks for a 2- or 3-mark question.

Remember

To get two marks you either need to:

(a) give two/three separate clear ideas OR

(b) develop one or two reason(s) more fully, perhaps giving more depth of detail.

How you get those two marks will depend on the style and nature of the question.

Identify why the following student answers do **not** get **3** marks for this question. At the moment they get 2 marks.

Describe how meanders are formed. (3)

A: A meander is a bend in a river. This is caused by erosion of the banks at certain points and the river becomes wider. Further erosion may create an oxbow lake.

This answer would not get 3 marks because ....

....

....

B: Meanders are formed when water continually hits the outside bend of a river causing it to erode.

This answer would not get 3 marks because ....

....

....

Activity 5: 2- or 3-mark questions

Look at the student answers for each question on page 48. For each answer:

- highlight in green a brief point
- highlight in blue support for a brief point
- highlight in yellow any comment/point that you think is irrelevant or an unnecessary repetition
- decide how many marks you should give each student answer.

1. *Outline one way in which rivers transport their load. (2)*

Student answers		Mark
A	Solution is where chemicals are actually dissolved in the river whereas tiny particles of sediment are carried in suspension in the river's current.	
B	Attention is one way in which materials are transported. They bounce into each other and become gradually smoother as they move down the river channel.	
C	A 'skipping' motion causes smaller pebbles and stones to be picked up and dropped again.	
D	Large stones are dragged along the bed of a river by the flow of the water. This is called traction. Faster flows and increased discharge means that more sediment is moved. This can happen under flood conditions.	

2. *Briefly describe the changes in river channel shape from source to mouth. (3)*

Student answers		Mark
A	The source of a river flows fast as rivers mainly start at the top of a hill. In the middle the river meanders. At the mouth the water slows down and is shallow.	
B	In the upper course the river is wide and deep, as you move towards the middle and lower courses the channel shape changes to become shallower and deeper.	
C	In the upper course the stream bed has many rocks as it starts in the mountains. In the middle section the river is deeper but has meanders. In the lower section it is straight and deep and very wide.	
D	Rivers tend to have an increasing channel cross sectional area as you move from the upper sections to the lower sections. They become wider and deeper and are more efficient at transporting water (less friction).	

Activity 6: 6-mark questions

Hint

Look at the mark scheme on page 10 and remind yourself how you get marks for a 6-mark question. Think about 'building an answer' rather than just telling a case-study type story.

For **two different types of river hard defences, explain how they work. (6)*

Read the two student answers below to the question above. You are going to try and improve them.

Remember

You will need to develop ideas more fully for a 6-mark answer, spending probably 7–8 minutes answering it. You should write perhaps two paragraphs, somewhere in the region of 8–10 lines. A 6-mark question will be marked on three levels. These levels describe the general quality of the work. For this more extended writing you will also be assessed on the quality of written communication. This is identified by *. Please see page 10 for more information on levels.

Student answers	
A	Defence 1: Extra drains and culverts. These can be used to reduce the impact of the flood. Defence 2: Flood storage reservoirs (or dams) store water in the upper parts of stream catchments. They can be used for water supply and HEP generation.
B	Defence 1: Retaining wall and channels are a form of hard defences where channel sides are built up to protect the surrounding areas. This has been done in many areas including Shrewsbury, Shropshire. They work well but can be expensive to build and are unsightly. Defence 2: Realignment channels take water away from towns and cities by diverting the flow to somewhere else before it reaches them. The original course of the river is therefore altered by literally putting in a 'by-pass'. This has been done in many places, including parts of the UK.

1. Student answer A is falling short of full marks – only getting 1 or 2 marks. We need to add an extra sentence to Defence 1 and Defence 2 to get maximum marks (3 + 3) as the question asks for two types of defence. There are two pairs of sentences below for Defence 1 and Defence 2. Tick your choice to ensure top marks and then explain why.

   A Defence 1 – Soft engineering such as washland management is increasingly being used as it's very effective and tends to have a lower environmental impact. ☐

   B Defence 1 – They work by diverting the water elsewhere and so reducing the impact in a local area; however they may increase the amount of flooding downstream. ☐

   C Defence 2 – They work by acting as a regulated store of water so during a potential flood event water can be more slowly released into the catchment. ☐

   D Defence 2 – They work by protecting the rivers banks from erosion and can be cheaply and easily installed; they are low cost. ☐

   For Defence 1 I chose .... because ....

   ....

   For Defence 2 I chose .... because ....

   ....

2. Student answer B:

   a) Identify the strongest and weaker sentences for each defence. Highlight the strongest sentence in blue and the weakest in green.

   b) Now write a new sentence to replace each weak sentence. ....

   Defence 1 ....

   ....

   Defence 2 ....

   ....

Activity 7: 6-mark questions

1. Look at the student answers for the question below. For each answer:
   - highlight in green a brief point
   - highlight in blue support for a brief point
   - highlight in yellow any comment/point that you think is irrelevant or an unnecessary repetition
   - decide how many marks you should give each student answer and why.

**For a named location, explain how human actions have increased flood risk. (6)*

	Student answers	Mark	Reason
A	Surrounding Sheffield, UK, deforestation means that more surface runoff in that area has happened. Heavy precipitation fell in June and July leading to increased water levels. Deforestation was due to humans cutting down trees for more living space. The clearing of land meant that there is less permeable rock which resulted in increased surface runoff resulting in more flooding.		
B	In Chingford, Essex, people have built houses and factories on the low-lying flood plain in the last 30 years. Rainwater is unable to naturally drain away as concrete and tarmac are impermeable surfaces. This water is then quickly transported into drains and this also increases the flood risk. In Chingford, during the 2009 floods, heavy rain went into the drains that were blocked by leaves. Another contributing factor was that in the other part of the catchment, trees have been removed which has reduced the interception layer and increased the flashiness of the storm hydrograph.		
C	Tewkesbury is built on the top of a flood plain therefore it is at high risk from flooding. Due to impermeable concrete the water cannot go through via infiltration and therefore becomes surface run-off. Deforestation stops water being intercepted by the trees so it over-flows the river banks. In the Amazon rainforest they are having a similar problem as deforestation is happening. Here, surface runoff has increased dramatically.		

2. Using the question above and ideas from these three responses, build your own A-A* answer that you think would get maximum marks on a separate piece of paper.

Remember

Use your own case study material that you developed at the beginning of this section on page 45. These answers require a little more use of case study material than you have previously done before. Try to use a few selected facts and figures to support your answer. This adds depth. Use of paragraphs is also a good idea.

Section C

Topic 7 Oceans on the edge

This is the first option in Section C; you have either studied this option or Topic 8 Extreme climates (see pages 56–60). This topic is divided into two parts:

- the first part reveals how and why some marine ecosystems are threatened
- the second part is about increasing pressures and the options for sustainable management.

Hint

There are no named locations that you must study but you are expected to have looked at one named marine ecosystem (e.g. coral reefs or mangrove swamps). You will also need to have looked at a local-scale named case study in terms of increasing stress, as well as two other local case studies of marine management.

Remember

Remember that in some cases you will gain marks for adding extra detail to a basic point. Sometimes you'll be asked to give details of a particular area such as a country or topic. You will have learnt examples for these in your GCSE course. Use fact sheets to make sure you know your facts and build your knowledge. See page 6 for more information on this.

Activity 1: Fact sheet

Complete the fact sheet which identifies local and global ways of managing marine ecosystems. Give the names and locations where relevant.

	Local strategies / actions	Global strategies / actions
Example 1		
Example 2		

Activity 2: Key terms

There are a number of key concepts and definitions that you need to know to be confident in this section. The following will help you practise these. Circle the correct answer to each of these questions.

1. What are the long-term changes in global atmosphere conditions called?
   climate change **sea level rise** **anomalies**
2. What is the term for the number and variety of species found within a particular area?
   habitat **ecosystem** **biodiversity**
3. What does the pH scale measure?
   acidity/alkalinity **magnitude** **frequency**
4. What term describes the movement and re-use of important substances such as nitrogen in an ecosystem?
   specialised **cycle** **nutrient cycle** **sulphur cycle**
5. What is the commercial and usually large scale farming of fish and crustaceans called?
   agro-forestry **aquaculture** **commercial fishing**

Activity 3: Understanding the exam question

1. Look at the two example questions below and then look at the marks for each question.

   Example 1 *Give one example of a local strategy to protect a marine ecosystem. (2)*

   Example 2 *State what is meant by the term 'nutrient cycle'. (2)*

   How much would you expect to write in your answer? Circle your choice.

   - Two sentences
   - A paragraph
   - Two or three paragraphs

2. How long do you think you should spend answering this type of question? Circle your choice.

   - Less than 1 minute
   - 2–3 minutes
   - 4–5 minutes

3. For the two questions above:

   a) underline the command word
   b) highlight key words such as technical language or important parts of the question to include in your answer.

4. Now decide what type of question it is. You must choose from: **definition**, **example**, **assess**, or **explain**.

   Example 1 is a(n) .... question. This means ....

   ....

   Example 2 is a(n) .... question. This means..

   ....

Activity 4: 2- or 3- mark questions

Hint

Look at the mark scheme on page 8 and remind yourself how you get marks for a 2- or 3-mark question.

Identify the reason why the following student answers do **not** get **3** marks for the question. At the moment they get 2 marks.

Describe the threats to one named global ecosystem. (3)

Remember

To get two marks you either need to:

(a) give two/three separate clear ideas OR

(b) develop one or two reason(s) more fully, perhaps giving more depth of detail.

How you get those two marks will depend on the style and nature of the question.

A: People are overfishing the species as there is huge demand in many parts of the world for tropical fish which can fetch a high price at market. Also breeding grounds are being destroyed by development.

This answer would not get 3 marks because ....

....

B: In coral reefs, tourism is a double-edged sword. It brings cash benefits to local people, but the building of hotels, etc. at the coast is environmentally destructive.

This answer would not get 3 marks because ....

....

Activity 5: 2- or 3-mark questions

Look at the student answers for each question below. For each answer:

- highlight in green a brief point
- highlight in blue support for a brief point
- highlight in yellow any comment/point that you think is irrelevant or an unnecessary repetition
- decide how many marks you should give each student answer.

1. *Define the term overfishing. (2)*

	Student answers	Mark
A	Overfishing is when people fish too much and there is less fish, the population of fish has gone down due to overfishing. The EU has come up with a plan to keep the numbers of fish the same so that they don't become extinct.	
B	When too many fish are taken from the ocean/river so that the fish population cannot be maintained and the numbers decrease in the longer term, e.g. tuna.	
C	Overfishing is when a species or habitat sees a large increase in catches. Cod, for example, has been caught for many years and is now being fished at an alarming rate. As the population is dwindling new laws have been put in place to stop it.	
D	Fish stocks are a sustainable resource, but overfishing is taking more of that resource than can be naturally replaced over time leading to long-term decline in fish stocks.	

2. *Describe the benefits that marine ecosystems can bring to local people. (3)*

	Student answers	Mark
A	Coral reefs, for example, can be very important for tourism, e.g. in Australia. People come on holiday and spend money in the local area which brings in foreign currency and helps the locals.	
B	Fishing is a very important source of benefits, e.g. cod in the north sea provides jobs when fish are landed in local markets; also jobs for fishermen. Coral reefs, e.g. in SE Asia, can be a local medicine source and help protect local people from storms acting as a buffer zone.	
C	Coral reefs supply tropical fish, seahorses and plants to the aquarium trade, e.g. in Plymouth Aquarium, England they have a tropical zone where many of these plants and animals have been imported. This is benefitting people in Plymouth as they can go and see them, rather than having to travel.	

Activity 6: 6-mark questions

Hint

Look at the mark scheme on page 10 and remind yourself how you get marks for a 6-mark question. Think about 'building an answer' rather than just telling a case-study type story.

Remember

You will need to develop ideas more fully for a 6-mark answer, spending probably 7–8 minutes answering it. You should write perhaps two paragraphs, somewhere in the region of 8–10 lines. A 6-mark question will be marked on three levels. These levels describe the general quality of the work. For this more extended writing you will also be assessed on the quality of your written communication. This is identified by *.

1. Look at the student answers for each question below. For each answer:
   - highlight in green a brief point
   - highlight in blue support for a brief point
   - highlight in yellow any comment/point that you think is irrelevant or an unnecessary repetition
   - decide how many marks you should give each student answer and why.

   a) **Explain how climate change is adding stress to marine ecosystems. (6)*

	Student answers	Mark	Reason
A	Climate change is affecting marine ecosystems because the temperature of the oceans is increasing. This is linked to acidification which may cause some species to become rarer. If there is acidification some plants in the ocean may not be able to grow due to this. Also, increasing temperatures = thermal expansions thus causing sea levels to rise and leading to more flooding.		
B	Higher temperatures cause more fresh water to enter the sea, affecting the pH which can stress some marine ecosystems. Coral reefs depend on a constant climate and increasing temperatures causes bleaching by removing the algae that live with them. Corals are part of a complex ecosystem and their destruction will have other impacts on the complex ecosystem which has a high biodiversity value. Climate change may also increase the intensity of tropical storms, e.g. around Florida, which can also damage the sensitive Everglades coastal wetlands ecosystem which is already stressed by human development.		
C	Increased temperatures result in higher sea levels due to ice caps melting. In the UK the greatest effects of climate change will be felt around the south east of England with a reduction in rainfall (causing rivers to dry up and stress to fish) as well as increased risk of storm surges. If the UK's water temperature increases, cod may move north to cooler waters – this will have an indirect impact on the fishing industry.		

b) *Using examples, explain how global actions are attempting to create sustainable marine ecosystems. (6)*

Student answers		Mark	Reason
A	In the North Sea, UNCLOS have been created to set maximum quotas for cod fishing so that there can be future catching without long-term damage. UNCLOS also manage large areas of the sea to try and prevent pollution. In 2002 a target was set for the development of Marine Protected Areas (MPAs) It was hoped that in the future these might help to protect 10% of the world's oceans. Lundy in the UK is an example of a 330 ha 'no take zone' – an MPA.		
B	People are catching endangered animals and looking after them from being killed and hunted. Also, some people are breeding marine animals to increase their numbers. This will help the ecosystem and other animals because they won't have to compete for food as much so other animals won't die out or even become endangered.		
C	In Australia at the Great Barrier Reef they have fishing laws. In St Lucia, global actions (SSMA) have been a successful model of sustainability, involving fisherman and businesses to bring people together. International action has provided frameworks for marine conservation. The Global Marine Species Assessment is part of that trying to find out what really lives in the sea. This will identify 'hotspots' and then inform decision makers at a global level.		

2. Using the questions above and ideas from the three responses, build your own A-A* answer that you think would get maximum marks on a separate piece of paper.

Remember

Use your own case study material that you developed at the beginning of this section on page 51. These answers require a little more use of case study material than you have previously done before. Try to use a few selected facts and figures to support your answer. This adds depth. Use of paragraphs is also a good idea.

Topic 8 Extreme climates

This is the second option in Section C; you have either studied this option or Topic 7 Oceans on the edge (see pages 51–55).

This topic is divided into two parts:

- the first part looks at extreme climates and their challenges
- the second part is about increasing threats and the options for sustainable management or protection.

Hint

There are no named locations that you must study but you are expected to have looked at one named extreme environment (e.g. polar – Alaska **or** hot / arid – the Sahel). You will also need to have looked at this as a local-scale named case study in terms of adaptations. You also need to have looked at the threats to a named ecosystem and the local and global actions.

Remember

In some cases you will gain marks for adding extra detail to a basic point. Sometimes you'll be asked to give details of a particular area such as a country or topic. You will have learnt examples for these in your GCSE course. Use fact sheets to make sure you know your facts and build your knowledge.

Activity 1: Fact sheets

1. Complete the fact sheet below to build up a local-scale extreme environment case study.

Name of extreme environment ....

	Details
Brief description of locations in a global context (countries and/ or regions)	
Brief facts about extreme nature of climate	
Adaptations (suggest a list of 3-4)	

2. Complete the fact sheet below to identify threats for two different examples; also include the local and global management options / actions. Give the names and locations where relevant; also facts and figures.

Threats case study

	Threats	Actions: local and global
Example 1		
Example 2		

Activity 2: Key terms

There are a number of key terms and definitions that you need to know to be confident in this section. The following will help you practise these. Circle the correct answer to each of these questions.

1. Which is of these is the odd one out?

   rainfall **drizzle** **snowmelt** **hail**

2. Which pair of words best describes a polar climate?

   treeless, <10°C average temperature **dry, >10°C average temperature**

   high biodiversity, about 10°C average temperature all year round

3. What term describes the degradation of land in arid or polar climates?

   desertification **denudation** **deindustrialisation**

Activity 3: Understanding the exam question

1. Look at the two example questions below and then look at the marks for each question.

   Example 1 *Give **one** reason why an increase in tourism may damage the culture of people living in an extreme climate. (2)*

   Example 2 *State what is meant by the term 'extreme climate'. (2)*

   How much would you expect to write in your answer? Circle your choice.

   - Two sentences
   - A paragraph
   - Two or three paragraphs

2. How long do you think you should spend answering this question? Circle your choice.

   - Less than 1 minute
   - 2–3 minutes
   - 4–5 minutes

3. For the two questions above:
   a) underline the command word
   b) highlight key words such as technical language or important parts of the question to include in your answer.

4. Now decide what type of question it is. You must choose from: **description**, **example**, **definition**, or **explain**.

   Example 1 is a(n) .... question. This means ....

   ....

   Example 2 is a(n) .... question. This means..............................

   ....

Activity 4: 2- or 3-mark questions

Hint

Look at the mark scheme on page 8 and remind yourself how you get marks for a 2- or 3-mark question.

Remember

To get two marks you either need to:

(a) give two/three separate clear ideas OR

(b) develop one or two reason(s) more fully, perhaps giving more depth of detail.

How you get those two marks will depend on the style and nature of the question.

Identify why the following student answers do **not** get **3** marks for the question. At the moment they get 2 marks.

Describe how people's clothing helps them survive in either extreme cold or extreme heat. (3)

A: Animal skins are worn to prevent people getting too cold. This happens in Alaska.

This answer would not get 3 marks because ....

....

B: In Australia modern fabrics help people stay cool in the heat of the day, these are combined with reflective white fabrics. They also have air conditioning in their houses which helps keep them cool.

This answer would not get 3 marks because ....

....

Activity 5: 2- or 3-mark questions

Look at the student answers for each question below. For each answer:

- highlight in green a brief point
- highlight in blue support for a brief point
- highlight in yellow any comment/point that you think is irrelevant or an unnecessary repetition
- decide how many marks you should give each student answer.

1. *Describe one way in which people living in an extreme climate have adapted to this environment. (2)*

Student answers		Mark
A	People have adapted to the extreme climate by wearing clothes that help their body cope with the climate.	
B	Locals have adapted by using alternative power such as solar energy – this is sustainable.	
C	In the driest parts of Australia, people have adapted by building artesian pumps which are used to extract groundwater from deep underground. This technology is important in an already dry climate that can suffer droughts. Air pressure is used to force water out through a pump.	
D	Tourism would have people coming to view the area and using vehicles which use fossil fuels rather than the aboriginals' preferred way of walking.	

2. *Explain how plants and animals have adapted to their extreme climates. (3)*

Student answers		Mark
A	In deserts, plants have adapted to dry conditions by reducing their demands for water through shedding leaves, for example. Animals such as the Red Kangaroo only feed at cooler times of the day to reduce water demand. In cold arctic conditions foxes have adapted by having white fur for camouflage.	
B	People use flat roofs to collect water in dry conditions (e.g. the morning dew). Plants in very cold conditions (which tend to be very dry) have reduced their leaf sizes to reduce the amount of water loss by transpiration.	
C	In polar regions plants grow close to the ground to avoid wind damage; they also have small leaves to minimise water loss. Whereas, in hot climates, some plants can have very deep roots to get at underground water supplies.	

Activity 6: 6-mark questions

Hint

Look at the mark scheme on page 10 and remind yourself how you get marks for a 6-mark question. Think about 'building an answer' rather than just telling a case-study type story.

Remember

You will need to develop ideas more fully for a 6 mark answer, spending probably 7–8 minutes answering it. You should write perhaps two paragraphs, somewhere in the region of 8–10 lines. Remember, a 6-mark question will be marked on three levels. These levels describe the general quality of the work. For this more extended writing you will also be assessed on the quality of your written communication. This is identified by *.

1. Look at the student answers for each question below. For each answer:
   - highlight in green a brief point
   - highlight in blue support for a brief point
   - highlight in yellow any comment/point that you think is irrelevant or an unnecessary repetition
   - decide how many marks you should give each student answer and why.

   a) **For either a named hot arid or a named polar region, explain the local actions which have been taken to help achieve sustainability. (6)*

Student answers		Mark	Reason
A	Named region: The Sahel. Solar panels have been installed, this increases the number of hours that people can work. This is a sustainable source of energy, i.e. it is renewable and does not require the use of fossil fuels. Also in the Sahel, agriculture has been managed in a much more sustainable way, including the use of diguettes. These have gone a long way to preventing soil erosion, e.g. in some areas of Burkina Faso soil depth has increased by 18 cm, whilst in other areas it has reduced.		

B	Named region: Africa. Oxfam helped a village in Africa to build field barriers as a way of catching rainwater and preventing soil erosion. This increased soil moisture and the village then started to carry out multi-crop farming. This involved planting a range of crops to reduce the risk of single crop failure. This was accompanied by the planting of fruit trees to increase interception and prevent soil erosion, thereby ensuring the future sustainability of the soil for other people and generations.		
C	Named region: Australia. The coast of Australia has been more urbanised to make it sustainable. More jobs are readily available and they are sustainable. In the desert areas jobs depend on weather conditions whereas in the cities people can work whatever the weather because of air conditioning. There is a more sustainable clean water supply.		

b) **For a named hot arid or polar region, explain how life is changing for its people. (6)*

Student answers		Mark	Reason
A	Named region: Australian outback. Life here is changing, tourism is coming into the region causing cultures of tribes to change. People are now using mobiles for example to communicate with each other (more 'western'). With the climate getting hotter and drier they are losing their crops – this means they are changing their crops to more drought resistant and using chemical treatments on their fruit. They are reducing livestock numbers for fear of overgrazing. El Nino is getting more frequent and this is bringing increasing drought and water shortages.		
B	Named region: Tanzania, Africa. The people of Tanzania have problems with a reliable water supply, however charities have helped people by supplying lined wells and hand-pumps. Tourism to see traditional rituals has impacted on the economy. Infection and disease is a big part of the life for people as the warm climate provides an ideal habitat for mosquitoes which have malaria. Aid has been given, however, in the form of medicines and mosquito nets to help prevent being bitten when asleep.		
C	Named region: Australia. Life for Australians is changing rapidly mostly due to the shortage of water there. This is all due to the great dividing range – a series of mountains on the east side of the country. Huge droughts are causing many people to move to the big cities in the hope of finding work. Farming is getting harder as there is a huge lack of water.		

2. Using the questions above and ideas from the three responses, build your own A-A* answer on a separate piece of paper.

Hint

Case studies should be specific, e.g. the Sahel rather than just Africa. This helps provide a focused answer typical of a Level 3 answer.

Remember

Use your own case study material that you developed at the beginning of this section on page 56. These answers require a little more use of case study material than you have previously done before. Try to use a few selected facts and figures to support your answer. This adds depth. Use of paragraphs is also a good idea.

Unit 2 People and the planet

Section A

Topic 1 Population dynamics

This topic is divided into two parts:

- the first part is about how and why population changes
- the second part is about how population changes can be managed by governments.

Remember

In some cases you will gain marks for adding extra detail to a basic point. Sometimes you'll be asked to give details of a particular area such as a country or topic. You will have learnt examples for these in your GCSE course. Use fact sheets to make sure you know your facts and build your knowledge.

Activity 1: Fact sheets

Complete the fact sheets below to build up an example of a pro-natalist case study and an anti-natalist case study.

Pro-natalist case study

Chosen country .... Dates/details ....

Reasons for policy (give data) ....

....

Details of policies ....

....

Impact/consequences of policies (give data) ....

....

Was it a success? ....

Anti-natalist case study

Chosen country .... Dates/details ....

Reasons for policy (give data) ....

....

Details of policies ....

....

Impact/consequences of policies (give data) ....

....

Was it a success? ....

Activity 2: Key terms

There are a number of key terms and definitions that you need to know to be confident in this section. Some of these key terms are given below. Match them to the definitions.

birth rate	**death rate**	**ageing population**
pro-natalist policies	**anti-natalist policies**	

1. Government action to encourage larger families ....
2. The number of children born per 1000 of the population in a year ....
3. When the average age of the population rises ....
4. Government action to encourage smaller families ....
5. The number of people who die per 1000 of the population in a year ....

Activity 3: Mark scheme for 2-mark questions

1. Read the following question.

   *Outline **one** reason why the rate of global population growth has slowed down. (2)*

   Write a mark scheme for this question.
   You should try to cover several possible 'basic' points to get 1 mark and suggest how these may be developed to get 2 marks.

   Mark scheme:

Hint

Have a look at the mark scheme example for a 2-mark question on page 8.

2. Now look at the two answers for the same question. What mark would you give these answers?

	Student answers	Mark
A	In many developing countries birth rate is falling because women are staying in education and seeking jobs.	
B	Since the 1980s better economies and more industry in countries such as China has made it less useful to have large families.	

Activity 4: 2-mark questions

Identify why the following student answers do **not** get **2** marks for this question.
At the moment they get 1 mark.

Outline one reason why some governments want to control population size. (2)

Remember

To get two marks you either need to:

(a) give two separate clear ideas OR

(b) develop one reason more fully, perhaps giving more depth of detail.

How you get those two marks will depend on the style and nature of the question.

A: The government can control population size using anti-natalist policies.

This answer would not get 2 marks because ....

....

B: The country has a problem with its population size.

This answer would not get 2 marks because ....

....

Activity 5: 2-mark questions

Look at the student answers for each question below. For each answer:

- highlight in green a brief point
- highlight in blue support for a brief point
- highlight in yellow any comment/point that you think is irrelevant or an unnecessary repetition
- decide how many marks you should give each student answer.

1. *Explain why some countries have high birth rates. (2)*

Student answers		Mark
A	In some countries governments encourage large families with more babies being born as a result.	
B	Some poor people need large numbers of children because they need them to work on the land.	
C	In Singapore there are a number of policies about population that have been tried and not all of them have worked.	
D	More children to work the land. Women may not have much choice because they aren't allowed education so they have to stay 'at home' and become mothers.	

2. *Outline **one** reason why a country may experience an ageing population. (2)*

Student answers		Mark
A	The UK has an ageing population because there are not many opportunities for young people here.	
B	If the birth rate falls then the average age of the population is likely to rise.	
C	Some older people have retired to Spain which obviously pushes up the age of population.	
D	Death rates have gone up because of AIDs and other diseases.	

Activity 6: 4-mark questions

Hint

Look at the mark scheme on page 9 and remind yourself how you get marks for a 4-mark question.

Remember

You will need to develop ideas more fully for a 4-mark answer, spending probably 4–5 minutes answering it. You should write about a paragraph, somewhere in the region of 7–8 lines. A 4-mark question is still point marked.

1. Read the student answers for the following question. For each answer:
   - highlight in green a brief point
   - highlight in blue support for a brief point
   - highlight in yellow any comment/point that you think is irrelevant or an unnecessary repetition
   - decide how many marks you should give each student answer.

   Using examples, describe how a government might try to encourage fewer births (an anti-natalist policy). (4)

	Student answers	Mark
A	In China they have a one-child policy which has been forced on people who are punished in various ways if they don't obey it. For families that go along with the government then they may get things like better education for their kids.	
B	China introduced the one-child policy in 1978. It offers rewards to families who limit themselves to one child and punishes those that do not agree with tax being lower for one-child families and much higher with fines for those that do not. In some cases force has been used and women have been sterilised.	
C	China's one child policy has reduced the birth rate by about half in 30 years. Other countries have just encouraged families to have fewer children such as Singapore which had a campaign saying that two children were enough, whether boys or girls. The smaller families got better education.	
D	There are many ways in which governments might try to encourage fewer births. Not all of these policies work and sometimes governments change their minds about their policies, e.g. Singapore. Governments can use punishments as in China or rewards. These can be many different things. Some might be better education and others might be higher or lower taxes. In China the result has been far too many boys and single men because many women aborted girls because they preferred to have boys. This is a problem for modern China.	

Activity 7: 4-mark questions

1. Read the student answers to the following 4-mark question and try to improve them.

Remember

Better answers are not necessarily longer answers but they are always more focused on the question. Key advice – keep it relevant and focused with no extra 'fluff'.

Explain why death rates vary from place to place. (4)

Death rates vary because of differences in the resources available in different places – places with few resources will have higher death rates. It might also vary because of variations in the age of a population.

This answer would currently get 3 marks. Which **two** of the following sentences would make this a full mark answer? Tick your choices.

A Death rate is the number of people per 100 of the population who die in any one period. ☐

B If food and water are in short supply death rates will usually be higher. ☑

C An older population is at greater risk of death so the rate is higher. ☑

D There are always more deaths in countries with larger populations. ☐

2. Now look at this student answer to the same question.

In some countries doctors are better trained so death rate is different. ①
Diseases such as AIDS have led to high death rates in parts of Africa. ②
War and the breakdown of basic services has led to higher death rates in Iraq and Afghanistan. ③

a) There are three sentences in this answer. Identify the weakest sentence and give your reason.

Sentence .... is the weakest because ....

....

b) Choose one of the sentences below to replace the weakest sentence. Tick your choice.

A Death rates are higher in countries with poor diet and water supply. ☐

B Death rate is higher in countries affected by war and civil unrest. ☐

Activity 8: 4-mark questions

1. The following student answer would currently get 2 marks for this 4-mark question.

   Explain why different migration policies may lead to tensions in a country. (4)

   Policies that stop people coming into a country may lead to a problem with the economy. Some economies don't need migrants but others do because they cannot develop without them. This is true in many countries in Europe where people can cross borders.

   Which **two** suggestions together would help raise this to a full mark answer? Tick your choice.

   A An example of the 'problems' that would arise in the economy. ☐

   B An example of the policies that would be in place to stop people coming. ☐

   C More details of migration movements within Europe. ☐

   D Some detail of what is meant by 'develop without them'. ☐

2. a) There are three sentences in this student answer. Put them in order of usefulness with 1 = most useful to 3 = least useful. Give a reason why you have put them in this order.

   Countries have many different types of migration policy that change over time. ①
   If they have an open-door policy this may lead to too many migrants arriving. ②
   There is often a tension between the need for more workers and the racist views of the existing population. ③

Sentence	Order of usefulness	Reason
1		
2		
3		

   b) Choose one of the sentences below to replace the weakest sentence and briefly explain the reason for your choice.

   A: The existing population may feel that its culture is under threat from 'foreign' ideas and opinions.

   B: Open-door policies mean that the government cannot control the type of migrants entering the country.

   I would replace the weakest sentence with sentence .... because ....

   ....

   ....

Topic 2 Consuming resources

This topic is divided into two parts:

- the first part is about how and why resource consumption varies from place to place
- the second part is about how sustainable the current pattern of supply and consumption might be.

Activity 1: Know your theories

Using **all** of the words and phrases from the box complete the sentences.
Each word and phrase an only be used once.

Hint

There are no 'case-studies' for this topic although examples are needed. However, you do need to know something about the various theories that cover the use of resources. This exercise is designed to test your understanding of these theories.

faster	**technical**	**necessity**	**invention**	**helped**	**resources**
economic	**population**	**famine**	**society**	**growth**	**shortages**

Malthus believed that as population increases .... than the supply of ...., especially food, it would eventually lead to severe .... of resources which, in turn might lead to ...., war and the breakdown of .... In order to prevent this happening he thought that poor people should not be .... because this might create further growth of population.

Malthus was wrong in his prediction about the supply of resources and both the 19th and 20th centuries saw very rapid .... growth and very rapid population .... Some academics, such as Ester Boserup, argue that .... growth might be a very good thing because as they grow and put pressure on resources we are almost forced to find .... solutions to shortages. Some people summarise this as '............................ being the mother of ....'.

Activity 2: Key terms

There are a number of key terms and definitions that you need to know to be confident in this section. Look at the key terms below and match them to the list of definitions.

renewable resources	**non-renewable resources**	
Malthus's theory	**Boserup's theory**	**sustainability**

1. The idea that population growth is good because it stimulates inventions and innovations that in turn increase production of food and other resources is called

   ....

2. Materials found in the natural world that will run out at current rates of consumption are called ....

3. The idea that the present generation should act in such a way that they meet their own needs without making it difficult for future generations to meet their needs is called

....

4. The idea that population growth will be faster than the growth in the supply of resources leading to disastrous famines and perhaps war is called ....

5. Materials found in the natural world that will not run out because their supply is infinite are called ....

Activity 3: Mark scheme for 2-mark questions

1. Read the following question.

   Outline one reason why the demand for some resources might fall in the future. (2)

   Write a mark scheme for this question.
   You should try to cover several possible 'basic' points to get 1 mark and suggest how these may be developed to get 2 marks.

Hint

Have a look at the mark scheme example for a 2-mark question on page 8.

Mark scheme:

2. Now look at the two answers to the same question. What mark would you give these answers?

Student answers		Mark
A	If we developed biofuels such as recycling cooking oils or making fuel from algae for internal combustion engines, the oil demand would be reduced.	
B	We have only just begun to recycle. Better technology in packaging and preserving food would cut back on the energy needed.	

Activity 4: 2-mark questions

Identify the reason why the following student answers do **not** get **2** marks for the question. At the moment they get 1 mark.

Outline why the demand for one named resource is increasing. (2)

Remember

To get two marks you either need to:

(a) give two separate clear ideas OR

(b) develop one reason more fully, perhaps giving more depth of detail.

How you get those two marks will depend on the style and nature of the question.

A: More people want it all the time.

This answer would not get 2 marks because ....

....

B: Because the supply is limited and demand is rising.

This answer would not get 2 marks because ....

....

Activity 5: 2-mark questions

Look at the student answers for each question below. For each answer:

- highlight in green a brief point
- highlight in blue support for a brief point
- highlight in yellow any comment/point that you think is irrelevant or an unnecessary repetition
- decide how many marks you should give each student answer.

1. *Describe Malthus's theory about population growth and resources. (2)*

Student answers		Mark
A	Malthus's theory about population growth says that we will run out of resources, so trouble will happen in a society.	
B	Poor people have large numbers of children. As a result there isn't enough food to go around.	
C	This says that population grows fast. However, we are smart enough to discover new things like GM foods.	
D	Population grows faster than food supply, so famines and war will happen unless the growth is prevented.	

2. *For a named resource, explain why production may fall in the future. (2)*

Student answers		Mark
A	Named resource: Oil The demand for oil is very high. That is because many people own cars and more people are buying them all the time.	
B	Named resource: Coal Coal is very dirty and doesn't help global warming, so other fuels are being used instead of it like oil.	
C	Named resource: Oil We are running out of oil. Many oil fields have already run dry because demand has gone up so fast.	
D	Named resource: Oil Oil is running out so we cannot produce as much. An example of this is the USA.	

Activity 6: 4-mark questions

Hint

Look at the mark scheme on page 9 and remind yourself how you get marks for a 4-mark question.

Remember

You will need to develop ideas more fully for a 4-mark answer, spending probably 4–5 minutes answering it. You should write about a paragraph, somewhere in the region of 7–8 lines. A 4-mark question is still point marked.

1. Read the student answers for the following questions. For each answer:
   - highlight in green a brief point
   - highlight in blue support for a brief point
   - highlight in yellow any comment/point that you think is irrelevant or an unnecessary repetition
   - decide how many marks you should give each student answer.

Describe how technology might solve the problem of resource shortages. (4)

	Student answers	Mark
A	Technology might develop because population growth forces us to think of new technology. This is Boserup's theory. An example of this working is the green revolution. This is producing better seeds which increase food production.	
B	Many people think the hydrogen economy will solve the problem of 'peak oil'. We are running out of oil. We depend upon it for transport and many companies want to develop fuel from water but it is very expensive at the moment.	
C	There are many problems that result from shortages of resources. Technology is very complicated but might help. An example would be solar power. Lots of people think that this won't work.	
D	We are running out of many different resources and there is a lot of pressure to replace them when they run out. Oil is a particular problem because we have used almost all of the cheap oil and are actively looking to replace it. We might invent new power sources like fusion power which will solve the problem. We might also find ways to replace oil like biofuels such as green alga. Unfortunately not all of these technologies are easy or cheap to develop.	

Activity 7: 4-mark questions

1. a) Read the student answers to the following 4-mark question and try to improve them.

> **Remember**
> Better answers are not necessarily longer answers but they are always more focused on the question. Keep them relevant!

Explain the problems of switching from non-renewable resources, such as oil, to renewable resources. (4)

Oil is running out very fast indeed and may not last until 2050.① Replacing it is difficult because alternatives such as hydrogen are expensive to produce.② We also don't have places like garages to provide this fuel.③ All the present technology is set-up for oil and it would be better to produce something like it.④

This answer scores 3 marks. Identify a sentence that you would **remove** from this answer and provide a reason.

I would remove sentence .... because ....

....

b) Which **two** of the following sentences would make this a full mark answer? Tick your choice.

- A The development of new fuel types is very expensive indeed. ☐
- B Unfortunately Trans-national Corporations aren't interested in developing new technologies. ☐
- C Some replacement fuels such as biofuels might cause more problems for the environment. ☐
- D In a recession governments may not be able to fund expensive research. ☐

2. Now look at this student answer for the same question.

Everything we have is set up for using oil from cars to all the stuff we make from it.① 70% of oil is used in transport so all the engines and motors are designed to use oil.② This makes it very expensive to replace this fuel.③

a) There are three sentences in this answer. Identify the weakest sentence and give your reason.

The weakest sentence is sentence .... because ....

....

b) Choose one of the sentences below to replace the weakest sentence. Tick your choice.

- A Hydrogen technology raises problems of safety because it is explosive ☐
- B It wouldn't be easy to replace plastic and all the stuff we make from oil. ☐

Activity 8: 4-mark questions

1. The following student answer currently gets 3 marks for this 4-mark question.

   For a named resource, describe the inequalities in its supply and its consumption. (4)

   Named resource: Oil
   There are many inequalities in the supply and consumption of oil. It isn't found everywhere with none in Switzerland for example, but a lot in the middle-east. Richer places use more because they can afford more things

   Which **two** of the following suggestions would most help improve this answer? Tick your choice.

   A An example of low consuming countries and/or global regions. ☐

   B A reason or reasons why oil isn't found in all locations. ☐

   C More detail of the 'things' that people have in richer places. ☐

   D An example of high consuming countries and/or global regions. ☐

2. There are three sentences in this answer. Put them in order of usefulness with 1 = most useful to 3 = least useful. Give a reason why you have put them in this order.

   Named resource: Oil
   Oil consumption is high in countries where people are wealthy and buy goods such as cars which take oil to produce and to use. ① In poorer countries they do not have these things. ② Some rich countries such as the USA are also very wasteful in their use of oil which is not taxed heavily so more is used. ③

Sentence	Order of usefulness	Reason
1		
2		
3		

3. Choose one of the sentences below to replace the weakest sentence and briefly explain the reason for your choice.

   A: In some areas cities have been built which depend on cars, for example, Las Vegas which uses vast amounts of oil.

   B: Oil is found in rocks that are not found in all places, for example, none is found in deep oceans.

   I would replace the weakest sentence with sentence .... because ....

   ....

   ....

Topic 3 Living spaces

This topic is divided into two parts:

- the first part is about what makes an area attractive to people and how that varies between and amongst different groups.
- the second part tackles the issue of how we can make living spaces more sustainable.

Activity 1: Fact sheets

Hint

You don't need to know about any particular location to do well in this topic. But you do need to have some knowledge of some **types** of location which you have probably studied through the use of specific, named places.

Remember

In some cases you will gain marks for adding extra detail to a basic point. Sometimes you'll be asked to give details of a particular area such as a country or topic. You will have learnt examples for these in your GCSE course. Use fact sheets to make sure you know your facts and build your knowledge.

Look at the following fact sheets and fill in the details.

Rural area 'under pressure' 1

Developed country .... Spain ....

Chosen rural area .... SE of Spain ....

Reasons why it is under pressure

1 .... UK retired people are moving to SE of Spain after retirement and are taking up housing spaces which can't be used for the Spanish citizens ....

2 ....

3 ....

Rural area 'under pressure' 2

Developed country ....

Chosen rural area ....

Reasons why it is under pressure

1 ....

2 ....

3 ....

Urban space in demand

Chosen city ....

Reasons why demand is rising for this living space

1 ....

2 ....

3 ....

Possible impact of this rising demand – will it make the area less attractive?

....

....

....

A more suitable living space

Chosen example of a more sustainable living space ....

Reasons why it is 'more sustainable'

1 ....

2 ....

3 ....

Activity 2: Key terms

There are a number of key terms and definitions that you need to know to be confident in this section. Some of these key terms are given below. Match them to the definitions.

the rural idyll **the 'rush for the towns'**
re-urbanisation **retirement migration** **sustainable cities**

1. Moving overseas when stopping work ....
2. The large scale movement of people from rural areas to cities, especially in developing countries ....
3. Urban areas that have a relatively small impact on the environment because of attempts to reduce resource consumption ....
4. The recent trend of growth for some cities, especially in the developed world ....
5. A commonly held romantic view that villages and the countryside are almost perfect places to live ....

Activity 3: Mark scheme for 2-mark questions

1. Read the following question.

   Identify ***one*** *problem of rapid urbanisation in developing countries. (2)*

   Write a mark scheme for this question. You should try to cover several possible 'basic' points to get 1 mark and suggest how these may be developed to get 2 marks.

Hint

Have a look at the mark scheme example for a 2-mark question on page 8.

Mark scheme:

2. Now look at the two answers to the same question. What mark would you give these answers?

	Student answers	Mark
A	In Mumbai about 1000 migrants arrive in the city every day from rural areas. They add to existing problems of poor housing and waste management.	
B	Slums such as Dharavi are already overcrowded and there are too few jobs for people. New arrivals cannot find the good jobs that they dream about.	

Activity 4: 2-mark questions

Identify the reason why the following student answers do **not** get **2** marks for this question. At the moment they get 1 mark.

Describe one way in which a city may become more sustainable. (2)

Remember

To get two marks you either need to:

(a) give two separate clear ideas OR

(b) develop one reason more fully, perhaps giving more depth of detail.

How you get those two marks will depend on the style and nature of the question.

A: They could introduce recycling schemes and improve public transport.

This answer would not get 2 marks because ....

....

B: They could spend money on upgrading the public transport system.

This answer would not get 2 marks because ....

....

Activity 5: 2-mark questions

Look at the student answers for each question below. For each answer:

- highlight in green a brief point
- highlight in blue support for a brief point
- highlight in yellow any comment/point that you think is irrelevant or an unnecessary repetition
- decide how many marks you should give each student answer.

1. *Explain one pressure resulting from a rising demand for urban living spaces. (2)*

	Student answers	Mark
A	If too many people move into cities it can all become difficult. Prices of houses can rise which is good for some people but not for others.	
B	Young people have moved to London. This is because the jobs are there.	
C	House prices might rise as demand rises. This can force out certain groups of people including those who grew up in the area, like in the London Olympics area.	
D	Rural areas lose population because there aren't enough jobs. This can lead to problems like closing services in villages and small towns.	

2. *For a named resource, explain why production may fall in the future. (2)*

	Student answers	Mark
A	Lots of English villages have falling populations. The people who leave are often young so the population is ageing.	
B	There are many problems in the rural areas of developing countries. Some of these are more difficult to solve than others.	
C	More second homes can mean fewer chances for local people to buy houses. An example of this is the Lake District.	
D	Many young people have left rural areas of India. This causes problems because only old people are left behind.	

Activity 6: 4-mark questions

Hint

Look at the mark scheme on page 9 and remind yourself how you get marks for a 4-mark question.

Remember

You will need to develop ideas more fully for a 4-mark answer, spending probably 4–5 minutes answering it. You should write about a paragraph, somewhere in the region of 7–8 lines. A 4-mark question is still point marked.

Read the student answers for the question below. For each answer:

- highlight in green a brief point
- highlight in blue support for a brief point
- highlight in yellow any comment/point that you think is irrelevant or an unnecessary repetition
- decide how many marks you should give each student answer.

Using examples, explain why some urban living spaces are in great demand. (4)

Student answers		Mark
A	Urban living spaces are in great demand for many reasons. Many parts of London are popular because young people want to be there. Jobs have come back to the city because of the growth of finance and business. Other urban areas have also grown such as Manchester.	
B	The growth of Mumbai has been very fast with most people coming from rural areas. All the best jobs are in cities and that is why people arrive. They live in shanty towns such as Dharavi. Many of them are disappointed with the reality of urban life rather than their dream.	
C	Some large cities such as London have grown in recent years mostly because of people moving in. The best jobs are there and redevelopment has provided more housing too. Urban areas provide more facilities such as clubs and bars. Sometimes it is cheaper to live in these areas because transport is more available than in rural areas.	

Activity 7: 4-mark questions

1. a) Read the student answer to the following 4-mark question and try to improve it.

Using examples, explain the attractions and disadvantages of migration when people retire. (4)

Many British people migrate to countries such as Spain when they retire. ① Spain is popular for retirement because it has a warmer climate. ② It also has cheaper property so people can sell British property and buy more cheaply increasing their savings. ③ However it means separation from friends and family. ④

Remember

Better answers are not necessarily longer answers but they are always more focused on the question. Some questions ask you to consider two different themes as this one does. The mark scheme is bound to reflect this!

This answer scores 3 marks. Identify a sentence that you would **remove** from this answer and provide a reason.

I would remove sentence .... because ....

....

b) Which **two** of the following sentences together would make this a full mark answer? Tick your choices.

A Unfortunately it can become more expensive if the pound falls against the euro. ☐

B It is also an attractive place to live. ☐

C Retirement allows people to choose where they wish to live if they have the money. ☐

D There is a well-established British community there as well. ☐

2. Read the following question and student answer.

Explain why the quality of living spaces in some rural areas is under increasing pressure. (4)

The growth of urban areas has made a big difference to some rural areas. Urban sprawl uses up farmland and changes local villages. These changes can affect people badly with jobs being lost. House prices might rise as well.

Which **two** of the following suggestions would most help improve this answer? Tick your choices.

A An example of a rural area under pressure. ☐

B An example of the changes that take place in villages. ☐

C More detail of the reasons for urban sprawl. ☐

D More detail on how people are 'affected badly'. ☐

Activity 8: 4-mark questions

1. Read the following question and the student answer.

For a named example, describe how living spaces can be made more sustainable. (4)

Barcelona has introduced 'bicing' which is sustainable. ① You can pick them up in one place and drop them off at another which is convenient. ② Obviously this helps the city's carbon footprint. ③

There are three sentences in this answer. Put them in order of usefulness with 1 = most useful to 3 = least useful. Give a reason why you have put them in this order.

Sentence	Order of usefulness	Reason
1		
2		
3		

2. Choose one of the sentences below to replace the weakest sentence and briefly explain the reason for your choice.

A: Bikes can be used for two hours and rent is free for the first 30 minutes.

B: Because people use bikes they are not using cars which means less fossil fuels are used.

I would replace the weakest sentence with sentence .... because ....

....

Topic 4 Making a living

This topic is divided into two parts:

- the first part is about how the world of work is changing fast and how these changes vary in different parts of the world
- the second part covers the impact of these changes on the environment and how we might be able to manage these changes more sustainably.

Activity 1: Fact sheets

Hint

You don't need to know about any one location to do well on this topic. But the examiners expect you to have some knowledge of places that have been affected by change so 'local' detail will be important. Remember that most mark schemes give credit for a relevant example.

Remember

In some cases you will gain marks for adding extra detail to a basic point. Sometimes you'll be asked to give details of a particular area such as a country or topic. You will have learnt examples for these in your GCSE course. Use fact sheets to make sure you know your facts and build your knowledge.

Fill in the following fact sheets using real places with some detail. If you can manage it, the detail should be related to your chosen example and not a general statement. For example, 'the car industry in the Midlands has declined' rather than 'manufacturing industry has declined'.

Employment changes in an industrialising country

Which industrialising country? ....

Identify three changes in employment

1 ....

2 ....

3 ....

Employment changes in a deindustrialising country

Which deindustrialising country? ....

Identify three changes in employment

1 ....

2 ....

3 ....

The environmental impact of economic change in the developed world

Which developed country? ....

Identify **two** environmental changes have taken place

1 ....

2 ....

The environmental impact of economic change in a city in the developing world

Which city in the developing world? ....

Identify **two** environmental changes which have taken place

1 ....

2 ....

Activity 2: Key terms

There are a number of key terms and definitions that you need to know to be confident in this section. Some of these key terms are given below. Match them to the definitions.

the Clarke-Fisher model	**deindustrialisation**	
rural diversification	**brownfield sites**	**'green' employment**

1. An attempt to describe changing employment structures as countries develop ....
2. Jobs that are created by attempts to find sustainable solutions to challenges faced by people ....
3. Where manufacturing jobs have been lost in a country, especially in cities ....
4. Areas in cities that have been used before but are now available for redevelopment ....
5. Attempts to create a wider range of jobs and opportunities in the countryside ....

Activity 3: Mark scheme for 2-mark questions

1. Read the following question.

   State ***two*** *characteristics of the quaternary sector. (2)*

Hint

Look at the mark scheme on page 8 and remind yourself how you get marks for a 2-mark question.

Write a mark scheme for this question. You should try to cover several possible 'basic' points to get 1 mark and suggest how these may be developed to get 2 marks.

Mark scheme:

2. Now look at the two answers to the same question. What mark would you give these answers?

Student answers		Mark
A	They tend to involve developing new ideas. They are often based on IT skills and software.	
B	This sector has developed more recently in developed countries. It is important because it creates new ideas and developments for industry to use such as new ways of using computers.	

Activity 4: 2-mark questions

1. Identify the reason why the following student answers do **not** get **2** marks for the question. At the moment they get 1 mark.

   Describe one way in which employment change in a rapidly growing city has affected the environment. (2)

Remember

To get two marks you either need to:

(a) give two separate clear ideas OR

(b) develop one reason more fully, perhaps giving more depth of detail.

How you get those two marks will depend on the style and nature of the question

A: There are many jobs in the informal sector such as market trading and street activities (e.g. shoe shining) and these are not always very well controlled.

This answer would not get 2 marks because ....

....

B: The growth of shanty towns in Mumbai has damaged the environment in many ways but in many ways life here is better than in poor rural areas because of the economic opportunities.

This answer would not get 2 marks because ....

....

Activity 5: 4-mark questions

Look at the student answers for the question on the next page.
For each answer:

- highlight in green a brief point
- highlight in blue support for a brief point
- highlight in yellow any comment/point that you think is irrelevant or an unnecessary repetition
- decide how many marks you should give each student answer.

Remember

You will need to develop ideas more fully for a 4-mark answer, spending probably 4–5 minutes answering it. You should write about a paragraph, somewhere in the region of 7–8 lines. A 4-mark question is still point marked.

Hint

Look at the mark scheme on page 9 and remind yourself how you get marks for a 4-mark question.

Using examples, explain the potential for growth of the 'green' employment sector. (4)

	Student answers	Mark
A	Green employment is employment that helps the environment in some way. An example would be people who work in jobs like designing wind turbines. Because this is a renewable source of energy it would help the environment. There are lots of other green jobs like in sustainable development.	
B	Green employment is employment in farming. Jobs in farming can be to do with organic farming which uses less chemicals. This is obviously good for the environment because less damage is done to it. Nitrates can wash off and go into the drinking water which isn't good.	
C	Green employment covers jobs that try to improve sustainability. An example is working in developing alternative energy like hydrogen fuel cells. Many car companies are spending money to do this. Another example would be work on recycling such as Singapore's NEWater scheme.	

Activity 6: 4-mark questions

Remember

Better answers are not necessarily longer answers but they are always more focused on the question. Keep them relevant!

1. a) Read the student answer to the following 4-mark question and try to improve it.

   Explain why some rural regions have become more diversified. (4)

Rural regions traditionally rely on farming but that industry has many problems and doesn't make as much money as it used to. ① Urban areas may seem more attractive because there is a wider range of jobs on offer there. ② Just to survive rural regions have to find other ways of making a living or they will eventually die. ③

This answer scores 3 marks. Identify a sentence that you would **remove** from this answer and provide a reason for your choice.

I would remove sentence .... because ....

....

....

b) Which **two** of the following sentences **individually** would make this a full-mark answer? Tick your choices.

A Without new industries young people will leave and income will fall. ☐

B Tourism is a very good industry to develop. ☐

C Farm incomes have fallen because subsidies have been reduced. ☐

D Diversification means finding some other way of earning a living. ☐

2. Read the following question and student answer.

Describe the changes in employment that take place as countries develop. (4)

In the beginning most people work in industries such as farming. All this changes when countries develop. Manufacturing develops such as the industrial revolution in the UK when an iron and steel industry developed. There is also a growth of tertiary industry. These days the most developed countries have few manufacturing industries left.

Which **two** of the following suggestions **together** would most help improve this answer? Tick your choices.

A An example of what is meant by tertiary industry. ☐

B An explanation about why manufacturing develops. ☐

C Another example of manufacturing industry. ☐

D Something about the development of the quaternary sector. ☐

Activity 7: 4-mark questions

1. Look at the question below and the student answer.

Using examples, explain how the growth of industries in developing countries can bring both advantages and disadvantages. (4)

China is a good example of a country that has developed a lot of industry in the last few years. ① This has brought a lot of money to China which has led to rapid economic growth. ② Not everyone thinks this is good as the USA is a big competitor. ③ The big problem is the damage to the environment which has happened in the cities especially. ④

There are four sentences in this answer. Put them in order of usefulness with 1 = most useful to 4 = least useful. Give a reason why you have put them in this order.

Sentence	Order of usefulness	Reason
1		
2		
3		
4		

2. Choose one of the sentences below to replace the weakest sentence and briefly explain the reason for your choice.

A: China's growth has been based on coal burning power stations which make China one of the worst polluters and has lead to health problems in the cities.

B: There are many people who don't like the number of Chinese goods in the shops and some of them have protested about it in stores such as Walmart.

I would replace the weakest sentence with sentence .... because ....

....

Section B 

Topic 5 Changing cities

This is the first option in Section B; you have either studied this option or Topic 6 Changing countryside (see pages 89–94).

This topic is divided into two parts:

- the first part covers the environmental issues faced by cities
- the second part is about how these issues can be dealt with, in a sustainable way.

Activity 1: Fact sheets

Complete the following fact sheets to build up an example of a sustainable city.

Hint

There are no named cities that you must study but you are expected to have knowledge of one city which is attempting to reduce its eco-footprint, and some information about your 'local' city.

A sustainable city?

Chosen city ....

Identify **three** ways in which this city is reducing energy consumption.

1 ....

2 ....

3 ....

Identify **three** ways in which this city is reducing its production of waste.

1 ....

2 ....

3 ....

Now check that at least two of these examples have some local detail that is clearly from **your** city rather than **any** city.

Local knowledge

Chosen area ....

Identify **three** ways in which local transport might be made/has been made more sustainable.

1 ....

2 ....

3 ....

Identify **three** ways in which consumer behaviour might be made/has been made 'greener'.

1 ....

2 ....

3 ....

Check that your examples have some local detail – a named place or local organisation would be useful here.

Activity 2: Key terms

There are a number of key terms and definitions that you need to know to be confident in this section. Some of these key terms are given below. Match them to definitions.

eco-footprints	**green consumerism**	**sustainable transport**

1. The purchasing of goods that takes notice of the environmental impact of those goods. ....
2. The amount of space required to provide people who live in cities with water, food, shelter, fuel and space for waste disposal ....
3. Systems that reduce the use of private cars and increase use of greener, lower energy-using methods of movement ....

Activity 3: Mark scheme for 2-mark questions

1. Read the following question:

   *Outline **two** characteristics of the quaternary sector. (2)*

Hint

Have a look at the mark scheme example for a 2-mark question on page 8.

Write a mark scheme for this question. You should try to cover several possible 'basic' points to get 1 mark and suggest how these may be developed to get 2 marks.

Mark scheme:

2. Now look at the two answers to the same question. What mark would you give these answers?

Student answers		Mark
A	They tend to involve developing new ideas. They are often based on IT skills and software.	
B	This sector has developed more recently in developed countries. It is important because it creates new ideas and developments for industry to use such as new ways of using computers.	

Activity 4: 2-mark questions

Identify why the following student answers do **not** get **2** marks for this question. At the moment, A gets 1 mark and B gets 0 marks.

Define the term eco-footprint. (2)

A: The eco-footprint is the amount of waste and pollution a city produces.

This answer would not get 2 marks because ....

....

B: Cities with high eco-footprints are not sustainable.

This answer would not get 2 marks because ....

....

Remember

To get two marks you either need to:

(a) give two separate clear ideas OR

(b) develop one reason more fully, perhaps giving more depth of detail.

How you get those two marks will depend on the style and nature of the question.

Activity 5: 2-mark questions

Look at the student answers for each question below. For each answer:

- highlight in green a brief point
- highlight in blue support for a brief point
- highlight in yellow any comment/point that you think is irrelevant or an unnecessary repetition
- decide how many marks you should give each student answer.

1. *Suggest **one** reason why cities will have varied ecological footprints. (2)*

Student answers		Mark
A	Cities that have many manufacturing industries will have a higher eco-footprint than cities that don't.	
B	Some cities have tried to reduce the amount of waste produced. Other cities have tried to reduce the use of cars.	
C	Cities can recycle if governments encourage it. This reduces the amount going to landfill or to incinerators so reduces the land required.	
D	Not all cities are sustainable. Las Vegas has to import water from other regions as well as Lake Mead.	

2. *Outline **two** ways in which local governments can help reduce the use of cars in cities. (2)*

Student answers		Mark
A	In Toulouse they have developed a metro system which has reduced the use of cars in the city.	
B	A government could ban cars altogether. This would be difficult because it would be very unpopular with the people.	
C	Barcelona has good cheap public transport systems. It has also introduced a scheme to hire bikes.	
D	Local governments could encourage people to walk and help them out with subsidies.	

Activity 6: 6-mark questions

Read the following student answers to the question below. For each answer:

- highlight in green a brief point
- highlight in blue support for a brief point
- highlight in yellow any comment/point that you think is irrelevant or an unnecessary repetition
- give the answer a mark and decide whether it should be in the top level, Level 3.

Remember

You will need to develop ideas more fully for a 6-mark answer, spending probably 7–8 minutes answering it. You should write perhaps two paragraphs, somewhere in the region of 8–10 lines. Remember, a 6-mark question will be marked on three levels. These levels describe the general quality of the work. For this more extended writing you will also be assessed on the quality of your written communication. This is indicated by *.

Hint

Look at the mark scheme on page 10 and remind yourself how you get marks for a 6-mark question.

**For a named city explain how it can reduce its energy consumption. (6)*

	Student answers	Mark
A	Singapore is a city of about 6 million people all crowded into a small island. They have pursued many policies to reduce their eco-footprint including some controversial ones. Their most famous policy is the congestion charging which charges people for taking their cars into the middle of the city. They have also done a lot of things about their water supply that are good. They have also recycled their water which helps the environment.	
B	Cities like Barcelona have spent a lot of money trying to improve their environment. So has London. In London the Bedzed project has reduced energy consumption. There are also schemes to improve how we get rid of waste with less waste being sent to landfill now that it is incinerated in heat and light projects. London has copied Barcelona by giving people bikes to get to work which obviously makes people fitter.	
C	If people install lots of energy conserving stuff then energy consumption will be reduced. This can be helped if people are given grants for insulation. Lots of people have installed solar panels too which save consuming fossil fuels and as a result the environment would be helped because of fewer carbon dioxide emissions. This is helpful for the whole world because of global warming. There are some cities in South America that grow their own food. An example is Cubita.	

Activity 7: 6-mark questions

> **Remember**
> Better answers are not necessarily longer answers but they are always more focused on the question. Keep it relevant!

1. Read the student answer to the following 6-mark question and try to improve it.

   **Explain why the eco-footprints of the cities of the developed world are so large. (6)*

   Eco-footprints are the amount of land used to support people's lifestyles. So if you use more stuff it makes more waste so eco-footprints are larger. Many cities have worked hard to reduce their eco-footprints. However, in general this is difficult in richer cities because people are used to consuming goods just because they can afford it. New York and London are both examples of developed cities.

   This answer would currently get 4 marks. Which **two** of the following sentences would raise this to a Level 3 answer? Tick your choices.

   A Because they are wealthy the people who live in developed cities often have two cars and expensive holidays. ☐

   B In the developing world people are poor so they are often unemployed and so don't have very much. ☐

   C Cities in the developed world are often larger and so they have bigger footprints. ☐

   D If cities have good policies like recycling and waste control systems they can reduce their eco-footprint significantly. ☐

2. Now look at this student answer which is for the same question.

   Cities in the developing world often have much lower footprints than those in the developed world. ① That is because they are very wasteful in the developed world and often don't recycle. ② They also use far too many things rather than saving and looking after the things that they buy, like mobiles. ③ Because people use more material goods in rich cities it would take much more land to supply all these things. ④ Cars are very expensive and wasteful because they pollute so much. ⑤ There are nearly 240 million cars in the USA for a population of 300 million. ⑥

   a) There are six sentences in this answer. Identify the strongest and weakest sentences and give your reasons.

      The strongest sentence is .... because ....

      ....

      The weakest sentence is .... because ....

      ....

   b) Choose one of the sentences below to replace the weakest sentence. Tick your choice.

      A Using cars burns oil so cities with more cars have high footprints. ☐

      B In some USA cities there is virtually no public transport so people have to use cars. ☐

Topic 6 Changing countryside

This is the second option in Section B; you have either studied this option or Topic 5 Changing cities (see pages 84–88).

This topic is divided into two parts:

- the first part covers the issues faced by rural areas
- the second part is about how these issues can be dealt with, in a sustainable way.

Activity 1: Fact sheets

Hint

There are no named rural areas that you must study but you are expected to have 'case-study' knowledge of specific rural areas relating to particular issues. You may have looked at different areas for each issue or question or combined them.

Remember

In some cases you will gain marks for adding extra detail to a basic point. Sometimes you'll be asked to give details of a particular area such as a country or topic. You will have learnt examples for these in your GCSE course. Use fact sheets to make sure you know your facts and build your knowledge.

Complete the fact sheets to build up examples of rural areas under pressure in developing and developed countries.

A rural area under pressure in a developing country

Chosen rural area ....

Identify **three** ways in which this area is declining and so under pressure.

1 ....

2 ....

3 ....

Identify **three** ways in which changes to the national and global economy affect this region.

1 ....

2 ....

3 ....

Identify **three** ways in which decline is being dealt with and comment on the sustainability of these projects.

1 ....

2 ....

3 ....

Now check that you have included some local detail that is clearly from **your** chosen rural area rather than **any** rural area.

A rural area under pressure in a developed country

Chosen rural area ....

Identify **three** ways in which this area is under pressure.

1 ....

2 ....

3 ....

Identify **three** ways in which urban areas may cause pressures in your chosen rural area.

1 ....

2 ....

3 ....

Identify **three** ways in which the pressures described are being managed and comment on their sustainability.

1 ....

2 ....

3 ....

Now check that you have included some local detail that is clearly from **your** chosen rural area rather than **any** rural area.

Activity 2: Key terms

There are a number of key terms and definitions that you need to know to be confident in this section. Some of these key terms are given below. Match them to definitions.

rural depopulation	**the changing global economy**	
second homes	**rural diversification**	**sustainable management**

1. A set of policies that look after present needs without harming the prospects of future generations to meet their needs ....
2. The loss of people from the countryside usually because of out-migration ....
3. These are houses owned by people whose permanent homes are somewhere else, often in a city ....
4. Policies and actions that create new job opportunities in areas once dominated by farming ....
5. The growing interlinking and interdependence of nations with more trade and movement of money and people between them ....

Activity 3: Mark scheme for 2-mark questions

1. Read the following question.

   *State **two** characteristics of isolated rural areas in developed countries. (2)*

   Write a mark scheme for this question.
   You should try to cover as wide a range of 'basic' points as possible to get 1 mark and suggest how these may be developed to get 2 marks.

Hint

Have a look at the mark scheme example for a 2-mark question on page 8.

Mark scheme:

2. Now look at the two answers to the same question. What mark would you give these answers?

	Student answers	Mark
A	They are often a long way from services and shops which make it expensive to live. There aren't many job opportunities because businesses don't want to be isolated.	
B	There are too few jobs in better paid professions so many people have to leave. It is hard to keep communities going because there are too few people to make it worthwhile opening clubs and bars and such like.	

Activity 4: 2-mark questions

Identify why the following student answers do **not** get **2** marks for this question. At the moment, A gets 1 mark and B gets 0 marks.

Define the term rural depopulation. (2)

Remember

To get two marks you either need to:

(a) give two separate clear ideas OR

(b) develop one reason more fully, perhaps giving more depth of detail.

How you get those two marks will depend on the style and nature of the question.

A: Rural depopulation is when people leave.

This answer would not get 2 marks because ....

....

B: Depopulation happens when there are not enough jobs for people.

This answer would not get 2 marks because ....

....

Activity 5: 2-mark questions

Look at the student answers for each question below. For each answer:

- highlight in green a brief point
- highlight in blue support for a brief point
- highlight in yellow any comment/point that you think is irrelevant or an unnecessary repetition
- decide how many marks you should give each student answer.

1. *Outline **one** reason why some rural areas are becoming depopulated. (2)*

Student answers		Mark
A	Some rural areas become depopulated because the industries are all in decline, such as farming.	
B	The growth of urban areas like London is important. It has led to a lot of commuting meaning people leave every day to work.	
C	In western China people are leaving rural areas. They migrate to cities like Shanghai where there is more work and more variety of jobs.	
D	Many rural areas in Africa have depopulated. This is because of civil war.	

2. *Describe **one** way how planners can help boost the economy of rural areas in the developing world. (2)*

Student answers		Mark
A	Planners have introduced lots of schemes to help rural regions. Not all of these have been successful because they often ignore local wishes.	
B	An example is a scheme that increases water supply, such as cost-effective boreholes in Mozambique. This helps local farmers and slows down depopulation.	
C	Governments may have schemes for distance learning. In Iceland broadband is supplied to rural regions that are very remote.	
D	Planners have encouraged micro-credit schemes such as the Grameen Bank. They have also developed the roads and power supply to remote regions.	

Activity 6: 6-mark questions

1. Read the following student answers to the question below. For each answer:
   - highlight in green a brief point
   - highlight in blue support for a brief point
   - highlight in yellow any comment/point that you think is irrelevant or an unnecessary repetition
   - give the answer a mark and decide whether it should be in the top level, Level 3.

Hint
Look at the mark scheme on page 10 and remind yourself how you get marks for a 6-mark question.

Remember
You will need to develop ideas more fully for a 6 mark answer, spending probably 7–8 minutes answering it. You should write perhaps two paragraphs, somewhere in the region of 8–10 lines. Remember, a 6-mark question will be marked on three levels. These levels describe the general quality of the work. For this more extended writing you will also be assessed on the quality of your written communication. This is indicated by *.

**Using examples, explain why some rural areas are under pressure from urban populations. (6)*

Student answers		Level/Mark
A	Rural areas close to cities such as Dorset often experience negative impacts from urban areas. If a region is in commuting range of the city then house prices will be higher; in Dorset they are about 30% higher than national averages. This means young locals cannot afford to buy properties so have to leave. This causes an older population. If the village is pretty like Corfe Castle then houses may be bought as second homes. These are only occupied occasionally so local services such as shops and schools suffer.	
B	Tourists can damage the environment. In the New Forest they often cause fires and kill the ponies by leaving plastic bags around. They frighten the wildlife and cause a lot of litter which is expensive to clear up. The New Forest is a National Park of nearly 600 km^2. There are many nearby urban areas including Southampton and London. Foreign visitors are also quite common. Tourists bring lots of money into the region but they also bring problems too.	
C	As cities grow they can affect rural areas in many different ways. Not all of these ways are good and many people don't like the impacts. Planners have to try to manage lots of different pressures. In order to do this they have to consider the needs of the local population. They also have to consider the needs of the visitors. Sometimes the needs of the visitors and locals are in conflict because economic factors such as jobs may not be easy to achieve as well as preserving the environment. An example of this is Scotland.	

Activity 7: 6-mark questions

> **Remember**
> Better answers are not necessarily longer answers but they are always more focused on the question. Keep them relevant!

1. Read the student answer to the following 6-mark question and try to improve it.

   **For a named rural area, explain how it could develop more sustainably in the future. (6)*

   Named rural area: Afar in Ethiopia
   The Afar region in Ethiopia is very poor. Ethiopia itself is a very poor country, 169th poorest in the world. Drought is a frequent threat and when it comes many people die. There have been many attempts to make the area more drought resistant. They have also provided small loans to improve local services such as shops. This is very similar to the Grameen bank micro-credit projects in many poor countries.

   This answer would currently get 4 marks. Which **two** of the following sentences would raise this to a full mark answer? Tick your choices.

   A The poverty is largely the result of local corruption and poor aid programmes that do not reach the proper people. ☐

   B In recent years FARM Africa has helped build irrigation channels to improve yields. ☐

   C Traditionally sustainable development is development that meets the needs of the present without stopping future generations from meeting their needs. ☐

   D If local health care can be improved by eradicating malaria using UN aid programmes then the area might develop from the bottom up. ☐

2. Now look at this student answer which is for the same question.

   Named rural area: The Sidamo region of Ethiopia is in the south of the country.① Ethiopia is very poor and local farmers in this region depend on coffee to make money to purchase all manner of things, including education for their children.② This is a real problem in this region because of a number of reasons. ③ Farmers have joined together to make a cooperative.④ That way they can sell direct to free trade companies to buy their coffee.⑤ That way they can get more than 20p for a kilo when it sells in Starbucks for about £200 a kilo!⑥

   a) There are six sentences in this answer. Identify the strongest and weakest sentences and give your reason.

      Sentence .... is the strongest because ....

      ....

      Sentence .... is the strongest because ....

      ....

   b) Choose one of the sentences below to replace the weakest sentence. Tick your choice.

      A The plan is to increase prices to about 50p a kilo which will allow local schools to be built and development to take place. ☐

      B The local farmers make so little from their coffee that they are forced to grow alternative crops such as the drug, chat. ☐

Section C

Topic 7 Development dilemmas

This is the first option in Section C; you have either studied this option or Topic 8 World of work (see pages 101–106).

This topic is divided into two parts:

- the first part covers the ways in which countries develop
- the second part is about how sustainable this development might be.

Activity 1: Fact sheets

Hint

There are no named development projects, countries or regions that you have to study but you do need examples of each of these so that you can respond to the 'For a named example…' 6-mark questions, and maybe offer an example in the shorter 2- or 3-mark questions.

Remember

Remember that in some cases you will gain marks for adding extra detail to a basic point. Sometimes you'll be asked to give details of a particular area such as a country or topic. You will have learnt examples for these in your GCSE course. Use fact sheets to make sure you know your stuff/build your knowledge.

Complete the fact sheets on development projects.

Regional differences in a developing country

Chosen developing country ....

Identify **three** economic differences between poorer and richer regions in the country.

1 ....

2 ....

3 ....

Identify **three** ways in which the urban core and rural periphery vary in this country.

1 ....

2 ....

3 ....

Now check that you have included some local detail that is clearly from **your** chosen rural area rather than **any** rural area.

Top-down development projects

Chosen top-down project ....

Identify **three** impacts of top-down projects on different groups of people.

1 ....

2 ....

3 ....

Suggest **one** reason why your top-down development scheme is helpful for developing countries and **one** reason why it isn't.

Helpful ....

Unhelpful ....

Bottom-up development projects

Chosen bottom-up project ....

Identify **three** impacts of bottom-up projects on different groups of people.

1 ....

2 ....

3 ....

Suggest **one** reason why your bottom-up development scheme is helpful for developing countries and **one** reason why it isn't

Helpful ....

Unhelpful ....

Activity 2: Key terms

There are a number of key terms and definitions that you need to know to be confident in this section. Some of these key terms are given below. Match them to the definitions.

economic development	**urban core and rural periphery**	
top-down development	**bottom-up development**	**sustainable development**

1. Development projects that are planned and controlled by local communities ....
2. Contrasts between rich cities and the poorer countryside and the relationship between them ....
3. Development that looks after present needs without damaging the prospects of future generations meeting their needs ....
4. Development projects that are planned and controlled by central government ....
5. The increase in wealth of a region or country due to greater production of goods and services ....

Activity 3: Mark scheme for 2-mark questions

1. Read the following question.

   **Define the term 'sustainable rural development'. (2)*

   Write a mark scheme for this question. In questions that ask for a definition you should try to indicate in the mark scheme what might be acceptable; it might be two different parts of a long definition or maybe a basic definition followed by an example.

Hint

Have a look at the mark scheme example for a 2-mark question on page 8.

Mark scheme:

2. Now look at the two answers to the same question. What mark would you give these answers?

Student answers		Mark
A	Sustainable rural development meets the needs of the present without creating problems for future generations to live in the same area because the resources have been reduced.	
B	Sustainable rural development projects try to preserve as much as possible without needless waste such as biogas projects in India which get rid of dung and night-soil whilst also preserving trees.	

Activity 4: 2-mark questions

Identify why the following student answers do **not** get **2** marks for this question. At the moment they get 1 mark.

Define the term top-down development. (2)

Remember

To get two marks you either need to:

(a) give two separate clear ideas OR

(b) develop one reason more fully, perhaps giving more depth of detail.

How you get those two marks will depend on the style and nature of the question.

A: A large project that often costs a lot of money.

This answer would not get 2 marks because ....

....

B: These are often big dams like the Three Gorges in China.

This answer would not get 2 marks because ....

....

Activity 5: 2-mark questions

Look at the student answers for each question below. For each answer:

- highlight in green a brief point
- highlight in blue support for a brief point
- highlight in yellow any comment/point that you think is irrelevant or an unnecessary repetition
- decide how many marks you should give each student answer.

1. *Outline **one** reason why top-down development may not always be popular with local communities. (2)*

Student answers		Mark
A	Local communities are not involved in making decisions. However, some of them may benefit with jobs.	
B	The Three Gorges Dam is an example of a top-down development project. These are very expensive and not always successful.	
C	Top-down development is controlled by the government and not local people so sometimes they don't take into account local needs.	
D	Top-down projects often mean that local people are ignored. This is unlike bottom-up projects which are developed by local people.	

2. *Describe **one** way in which bottom-up development can help local communities. (2)*

Student answers		Mark
A	Local communities can be helped more by bottom-up development than top-down development. This is because bottom-up development uses appropriate technology and not expensive material that cannot be serviced.	
B	Bottom-up development listens to local people who usually make the plans. The Grameen Bank has made micro-credit loans to many Bangladeshi women to start small businesses in their local communities.	
C	Bottom-up development is usually small scale but cheap to establish. There are many examples in Africa.	

Activity 6: 6-mark questions

1. Read the following student answers to the question below. For each answer:
   - highlight in green a brief point
   - highlight in blue support of a brief point
   - highlight in yellow any comment/point that you think is irrelevant or an unnecessary repetition
   - give the answer a mark and decide whether it should be in the top level, Level 3. Justify your choice.

Hint

Look at the mark scheme on page 10 and remind yourself how you get marks for a 6-mark question.

Remember

You will need to develop ideas more fully for a 6-mark answer, spending probably 7–8 minutes answering it. You should write perhaps two paragraphs, somewhere in the region of 8–10 lines. Remember, a 6-mark question will be marked on three levels. These levels describe the general quality of the work. For this more extended writing you will also be assessed on the quality of your written communication. This is indicated with *.

**For a named developing country, explain why 'bottom-up' development projects have both advantages and disadvantages. (6)*

	Student answers	Level/Mark
A	Ethiopia is one of the world's poorest countries with most people earning less than $2 a day. There are many efforts to help people with bottom-up development plans. An example is FARM Africa helping with the development of cost-effective boreholes that cost about $5000 each to bring water to local communities and so improve their production. Other charities have helped establish coffee co-operatives in Sidoma province. This helps to increases the income of farmers so that they can improve schools and other facilities.	
B	Bottom-up projects in Bangladesh have helped local communities. In villages close to Dhaka the Grameen Bank has lent local women money to establish businesses. These can be small shops or textile factories making cloth. Profits made have been used to set up more businesses as the Grameen Bank will only lend to groups of five borrowers. However, the country obviously needs some big projects too because bottom-up development will not create roads or power supplies for large areas. In particular, the country needs large projects to prevent flooding in coastal regions like the Sunderbans.	
C	Bottom-up projects have many advantages. Local communities like them because they have a part in the plans. They are often cheaper and the technology they use is suitable for the community so that it can look after it themselves. Top-down projects are much larger and organised by the government who often don't consult local communities – this was true of the Three Gorges Project in China. Sometimes local communities are very badly affected. In the case of the Three Gorges project over 1 million people had to be moved out of the flooded valleys.	

Activity 7: 6-mark questions

Look at the student answer to the following 6-mark question and try to improve it so that it reaches Level 3.

**For a named developing country, explain the differences between the urban cores and the rural periphery. (6)*

Remember

Better answers are not necessarily longer answers but they are always more focused on the question. Keep them relevant!

Named developing country: Bolivia

Bolivia is one of the most unequal countries in the world. A rich elite live mostly in the tropical lowlands with the poor living in the rural Altiplano. The poor are mostly native Americans who own very little but the rich are descendants of Spanish colonists and they own everything. Until recently they also controlled the government and all the resources.

This answer would currently get 4 marks. Which **two** of the following sentences would raise this to a full mark answer? Tick your choices.

A Cities such as La Paz and Cochabamba tend to be richer because business is controlled from there. ☐

B The average income is about $2000 per person but many native Americans are much poorer than this. ☐

C Since colonial days the resources have been sold to the benefit of the rich landowning class, many of whom have large houses in the cities. ☐

D Not all urban areas are richer. La Paz has a large shanty town, El Alto, which has a population of nearly 1 million rural-urban migrants. ☐

Activity 8: Guess the question

1. Read the following student answer and then select the question that the student was answering. Tick your choice.

   Bottom up development projects are often more successful than top-down projects. This is because they have the interest of local people and so they work hard to make them work. Not all top-down projects are bad though. Malawi uses World Bank funds to pay doctors much higher salaries (+50%) to fight aids, tuberculosis and malaria and to fund new training programmes. Twenty thousand women without nursing qualifications have been trained in maternal and child health and now work in rural areas. This has been hugely successful is bringing down disease. Without top-down projects like this, bottom up schemes would have no chance.

   A For a named country, describe why top-down development projects have both advantages and disadvantages. ☐

   B Using examples, compare the success of bottom-up and top-down development projects. ☐

   C Describe the different ways in which countries might choose to develop. ☐

2. Based on your answer to question 1, identify which **two** of the following the student should have done but didn't!

   A Offered more about bottom-up projects, with examples. ☐

   B Given more detail about the top-down health care programme. ☐

   C Used more comparative words such as 'less' and 'more'. ☐

   D Written about several different countries. ☐

Topic 8 World of work

This is the second option in Section C; you have either studied this option or Topic 7 Development dilemmas (pages 95–100).

This topic is divided into two parts.

- the first part covers the issues surrounding the emergence of the 'new economy'
- the second part is about how sustainable this 'new economy' might be.

Activity 1: Fact sheet

Hint

There are no named case studies but you do need an example of one TNC which you will have studied in class so that you can respond to the 'For a named example…' 6-mark questions and maybe offer an example in the shorter 2- or 3-mark questions.

Remember

In some cases you will gain marks for adding extra detail to a basic point. Sometimes you'll be asked to give details of a particular area such as a country or topic. You will have learnt examples for these in your GCSE course. Use fact sheets to make sure you know your facts and build your knowledge.

Complete the fact sheet on how transnational corporations (TNCs) operate and the advantages and disadvantages of TNCs.

Transnational corporations

Chosen TNC ....

Describe **three** ways in which the TNC organises its global operation.

1 ....

2 ....

3 ....

Identify **three** advantages that TNCs bring to developing countries.

1 ....

2 ....

3 ....

Identify **three** disadvantages that TNCs bring to developing countries.

1 ....

2 ....

3 ....

Identify **two** advantages that TNCs bring to developed countries.

1 ....

2 ....

Identify **two** disadvantages that TNCs bring to developed countries.

1 ....

2 ....

3 ....

Now check that you have included some local detail that is clearly from **your** chosen TNC rather than **any** TNC.

Activity 2: Key terms

There are a number of key terms and definitions that you need to know to be confident in this section. Some of these key terms are given below. Match them to the definitions.

the 'new economy'	transnational corporations (TNC)	global shift	outsourcing

1. The changes in the international division of labour with, for example, manufacturing shifting to NICs and finance and business services developing in the most developed countries ....
2. The shift of manufacturing and service jobs to countries with cheaper labour and government incentives ....
3. Large companies that set up part of their operation overseas ....
4. The different way that employment and production is now organised in a globalised world ....

Activity 3: Mark scheme for 2-mark questions

1. Read the following question.

   *Outline **one** change in the global economy that has created new types of employment. (2)*

Hint

Have a look at the mark scheme example for a 2-mark question on page 8.

Write a mark scheme for this question.
You should try to cover several possible 'basic' points to get 1 mark and suggest how these may be developed to get 2 marks.

Mark scheme:

2. Now look at the two answers to the same question. What mark would you give these answers?

Student answers		Mark
A	Communication using computers has allowed information to travel all over the world very fast. This has led to new types of banking and financial markets growing fast.	
B	Container goods made in China are delivered all over the world. This has led to manufacturing growing in NICs whereas in countries like the US and UK it is nanotechnology and biotechnology that has grown.	

Activity 4: 2-mark questions

Identify the reason why the following student answers do **not** get **2** marks for the question. At the moment they get 1 mark.

*Identify **two** features of Transnational Corporations (TNC). (2)*

> **Remember**
>
> To get two marks you either need to:
>
> (a) give two separate clear ideas OR
>
> (b) develop one reason more fully, perhaps giving more depth of detail.
>
> How you get those two marks will depend on the style and nature of the question.

A: A large company that makes different things.

This answer would not get 2 marks because ....

....

B: They are very unpopular because they make large profits

This answer would not get 2 marks because ....

....

Activity 5: 2-mark questions

Look at the student answers for each question below. For each answer:

- highlight in green a brief point
- highlight in blue support for a brief point
- highlight in yellow any comment/point that you think is irrelevant or an unnecessary repetition
- decide how many marks you should give each student answer.

1. *Define the term outsourcing. (2)*

Student answers		Mark
A	Outsourcing takes place because many developing countries have cheap labour, an example is China.	
B	Outsourcing happens when companies look for new places to operate because they need to make money.	
C	Outsourcing is when a TNC starts up production in another country, an example is Nike's factories in Vietnam.	
D	TNCs have many ways of reducing costs. Outsourcing is one of these.	

2. *Describe **one** feature of the 'new economy'. (2)*

Student answers		Mark
A	The new economy is changing everything. Jobs in manufacturing have gone and have been replaced by jobs in IT and the quaternary sector.	
B	Manufacturing jobs have shifted to NICs such as China and India. These have been replaced by service and quaternary jobs in countries such as Britain.	
C	Jobs are more and more insecure with people changing jobs many times and having to learn new skills as employment changes.	

Activity 6: 6-mark questions

Hint

Look at the mark scheme on page 10 and remind yourself how you get marks for a 6-mark question.

Remember

You will need to develop ideas more fully for a 6-mark answer, spending probably 7–8 minutes answering it. You should write perhaps two paragraphs, somewhere in the region of 8–10 lines. Remember, a 6-mark question will be marked on three levels. These levels describe the general quality of the work. For this more extended writing you will also be assessed on the quality of your written communication. This is indicated by *.

Read the following student answers to the question below. For each answer:

- highlight in green a brief point
- highlight in blue support for a brief point
- highlight in yellow any comment/point that you think is irrelevant or an unnecessary repetition
- give the answer a mark and decide whether it should be in the top level, Level 3. Justify your choice.

**Using examples, explain how the 'new economy' is affecting developed countries. (6)*

	Student answers	Level/Mark
A	In many developed countries such as the UK there are many changes in employment. There are about 31 people working in the UK. In recent years more of them have become part-time and many are in 'temporary' jobs with no permanent contract. The jobs have changed too with only 15% in manufacturing; some industries have pretty much gone like shipbuilding and coal mining. In developing countries there has been a rise in manufacturing jobs and many firms outsource to places like China.	
B	Jobs have been lost in manufacturing industry. In 1950 there were 35% employed in jobs like machine tools, car manufacture, shipbuilding and the UK was a big exporter. Today it is only 15% working in these types of jobs and many of these are working for foreign companies such as Honda in Swindon. There are many fewer of these jobs because of the use of robots – only 5000 people work in Honda producing 200,000 cars every year. A few years ago there would have been 20,000 people.	
C	Very big changes have taken place in rich countries. The growth of TNCs has changed completely where things are made today. Many more women go to work and the largest number of jobs is in the tertiary sector. Not all of these jobs are very well-paid or very secure but some of them are obviously better and there are rich people like bankers who don't make anything except debt but get big fat bonuses. Quite a lot of this money ends up in offshore bank accounts and doesn't help the country. Not all the TNCs pay the right amount of tax as well.	

Activity 7: 6-mark questions

Look at the student answer to the following 6-mark question and try to improve it so that it reaches Level 3.

**Using examples, explain why the impact of TNCs is not always positive. (6)*

Remember

Better answers are not necessarily longer answers but they are always more focused on the question. Keep them relevant!

TNCs have one main motive. That is to make money for shareholders who own these companies. Sometimes this can mean that they do things that are harmful to people and the environment like pollution and waste or even paying bad wages to people. Positive things might happen like cheaper goods and maybe some jobs are better than none but the overall effect is often negative.

This answer would currently get 4 marks. Which **two** of the following sentences would raise this to a full mark answer? Tick your choices.

A Ray Anderson at Interface carpets called the damage to the environment 'plundering' and has tried to make his company behave sustainably. ☐

B Critics of TNCs just have to accept that the bad things that are done are almost inevitable and that making a profit has to be a good thing in the long run. ☐

C When Levi-Strauss decided to move production out of the USA it shut down 14 factories making thousands unemployed in the USA; many of these people could not get new jobs. ☐

D Sustainable development is development that looks after the needs of the present generation without forgetting the needs of future generations. ☐

Activity 8: Guess the question

1. Read the following student answer and then select the question that the student was answering. Tick your choice.

   Most TNCs have their headquarters in their country of origin, so BP's HQ is in the UK and Samsung's is in South Korea. They operate in different parts of the world because they are constantly trying to reduce costs by outsourcing and maybe looking for new markets. BP operates wherever they can find oil but they also have a service sector in selling petrol. They don't always employ local people.

   A For a named TNC, explain why it operates in many different countries. ☐

   B For a named TNC, describe how the new economy operates in different parts of the world. ☐

   C For a named developing country, describe the impact of outsourcing and the growth of the service economy. ☐

2. Based on your answer to question 1, identify which **two** of the following the student should have done but didn't!

   A Offered more reasons for operating in many countries. ☐

   B Given a wider range of examples. ☐

   C Been much clearer about the 'named …' example. ☐

   D Written about several different countries. ☐

Introduction

p6 Focus

1. B
2. Describe the ways in which a government might control migration

p6 Restrictions

1. a) 'developed countries' b) 'in the past'
2. 'rapidly growing'

pp6–7 Putting it into practice

1. A: two sentences B: a paragraph
2. A: 2–3 minutes B: 4–5 minutes
3. Command word: A: State B: Outline
   Focus: A: Ocean crust characteristics
   B: Improving building design
4. Example A is a describe question. This means you should say what it is like, what it looks like
   Example B is an explain question. This means you give some detail about how this can be done

pp8–9 A 1 mark B 2 marks C 1 mark

pp9–10

1. 4 marks
2. Agriculture…decline but secondary industry…declines fast. In the last few years…grown up, these…IT and research.

p11

1. A TNCs are…. What was worse was that…used foreign labour.
   B TNCs…Vietnam but often wages…advantage is reduced. In some…the benefit is even less because…India but a disadvantage is that they…water supplies. So some…the disadvantages.
2. B The answers have similar facts and examples but answer B shows stronger evaluation skills than answer A.

Developing geographical skills

p12 Activity 1

A 1 mark – just a basic idea
B 2 marks – basic idea plus an example (carbon monoxide)
C 0 marks – no relevant comment – there aren't many people about

pp13–14 Activity 2

1. B: *uneven* = 1 mark; *distinct lines* = 1 mark
2. A
3. a)

Sentence	Order of usefulness
1	3
2	2
3	1

   b) Sentence A is the best replacement sentence.

p14 Activity 3

1. … they are the same idea.
2. C 3. B
4. a) C because the wells are responsible for the fall in water and the answer doesn't address 'impact'.
   b) B because it uses good geographical language, e.g. water table.

pp16–17 Activity 4

A Las Vegas has grown a great deal. Some of the growth has been to the north-west. 2 marks
B Las Vegas has exploded in … of the tourists. 1 mark
C There are many reasons … in many different ways. 0 marks
D Las Vegas has grown by about … the south. 2 marks

2. B and C
3. B because it identifies a key feature and gives added detail such as data and a description. It also uses better geographical language, e.g. sea wall.

pp18–19 Activity 5

1. A The population goes up most of the time. It sometimes doesn't when it hits the line. 2 marks
   B Population rises until it meets the resource line. It does go down sometimes quite regularly. 2 marks
   C Population falls … on rising. 0 marks
   D Food production rises as well as population. Then population falls quickly when it hits the resource line. 1 mark
2. a)

Sentence	Order of usefulness
1	2
2	1
3	3

   b) Sentence B is the best replacement sentence.
3. a) Methane b) B or D C A

Unit 1

Topic 1

p20 Activity 2

1. away 2. subduction 3. destructive power
4. they move slowly 5. evacuate the area

p21 Activity 3

1. 2 sentences
2. spend 2–3 minutes.
3. a) Example 1: Give Example 2: Outline
4. Example 1: example Example 2: explain

p21 Activity 4

A: Only one reason given (size – 'bigger') and reason is not developed.
B: Sweeping statement, there are emergency services, but they might not work very well or may be under-resourced.

p22 Activity 5

1. A They are generally not very violent…tall. 0 marks
   B They are often shaped as a cone…slowly. 2 marks
   C Shield volcanoes are found at destructive …highly explosive. There is a gradual build-up of runny lava. 1 mark
   D There is a steady accumulation of lava resulting in the flattish shape which can be very large in size. 2 marks
2. A They can hide under a table. 1 mark
   B People can build earthquake resistant buildings and houses which are shake-proof. 2 marks
   C Governments can get … earthquake. 1 mark
   D Authorities can produce action plans. These tell the … earthquake. 2 marks

pp22–23 Activity 6

A In the earthquake in 2008 … hour. Medical services tried to reach the area, however … destroyed. 2 marks
B In Kobe, Japan, … the area (preventing more fires and explosions in buildings) and to get medical … water and were relocated to refugee camps … destroyed. 4 marks
C In Japan … people. However the … volcanoes. The government … notified. 3 marks

pp23–24 Activity 7

1. A and C
2. a) Sentence 1 is the weakest because it doesn't directly link to the focus of the question.
   b) B
3. C and D
4.

Sentence	Order of usefulness
1	1
2	3
3	2

Topic 2

p26 Activity 2

1. sun-spot cycles volcanoes
2. Banglasdesh
3. smoking air travel

p26 Activity 3

1. 2 sentences
2. spend 2–3 minutes.
3. a) Example 1: What Example 2: Outline
4. Example 1: description Example 2: explain

p27 Activity 4

A: Developing countries do not always trade less (China – biggest exporter). Would need to give better examples.

B: Often the pollution law is very weak in developing countries.

Activity 5

1. A People were able to grow less food due to all the rain. 1 mark
   B Agricultural productivity was changed as a result of the Little Ice Age. 1 mark
   C Cold … less plants so there are less crops. 2 marks
   D Crops were frozen and there were the … Fairs. 1 mark
2. A Sometimes emissions from volcanoes can cause problems for people. 1 mark
   B Carbon dioxide … climate change. 0 marks
   C Sun-spot cycles cause changes in the earth's temperature. 2 marks
   D Distance the … Sun can vary … of time. 2 marks

p28 Activity 6

A Example: the UK. Ski resorts in Scotland could be affected with … beach tourism, good effect for local businesses. 3 marks

B In Bangladesh … to mean the country … the sea. People will have to move … rise. The ground will become infiltrated and they … crops. 2 marks

C Wildlife and plants will die … climate. My example … Ethiopia. People do not have … of water so dehydration … problem. They can't afford...climate change. 3 marks

pp28–29 Activity 7

1. C and D
2. a) Sentence 1 is the weakest because it repeats the question.
   b) B
3. C and A

Topic 3

p31 Activity 2

1. good
2. Greenpeace
3. sustainable

p31 Activity 3

1. 2 sentences
2. spend 2–3 minutes.
3. a) Example 1: Give Example 2: Outline
4. Example 1: example Example 2: description

p32 Activity 4

A: Only one reason given and the idea is not developed.

B: Timber is valuable (1 mark) but it's not always cheap and easy to chop down.

Activity 5

1. A You could develop a park … plant species; you can also stop … of footpath erosion. 1 mark
   B Ban all hunting of the area, this may make local people … to go without clothing.1 mark
   C Set up trade agreements, e.g. CITES to ban the sale or export of things … like ivory. 2 marks
   D Promote eco-tourism, e.g. in Africa, where people pay to … as trophies. 1 mark
2. A There is a loss of income for … forests are cut down (no more forest goods). 2 marks
   B Causes climate change by changing the reflectivity of a surface (albedo). 2 marks
   C Removal of the trees … the soil (nutrients); trees also protect … harsh weather. 2 marks
   D Trees are a cash crop. Their … big effect. 0 marks

p33 Activity 6

A The rainforest provides us with many goods and services including air to breathe and timber for making furniture. Other biomes also provide things. 2 marks

B Rainforests … goods such as medicines … types of food like berries and also raw materials, e.g. timber for construction. 3 marks

C Goods … such as food from seas or medicines from the rainforest. Services on the … types of soil. 1 mark

pp33–34 Activity 7

1. D and B
2. a) Sentence 3 is the weakest because it does not relate to factors that effect distribution.
   b) A
3. A and D

Sentence	Order of usefulness
1	1
2	3
3	2

Topic 4

p36 Activity 2

1. salinisation 2. abstraction 3. appropriate

p36 Activity 3

1. 2 sentences
2. spend 2–3 minutes.
3. a) Example 1: Suggest Example 2: Outline
4. Example 1: description Example 2: explain

p37 Activity 4

A: Use of vague terms, e.g. 'go round' which doesn't describe the fact that it is a closed system with interrelationships. Not everything goes into the sea or lakes, e.g. evaporation, role of rivers, etc.

B: There are inputs and outputs (1 mark), but this answer needs more to link it to the idea of a system, i.e. the role of interconnections, etc.

p36 Activity 5

1. A Boats emit wastes into the sea water … dirty. This ends up on beaches. 2 marks
   B Toxic waste is … the sea making it impure and dangerous. This waste … stations. 2 marks
   C Pollution of groundwater supplies can reduce water quality and hurt fish. 2 marks
   D Adding nitrate fertilisers, e.g. in … end up in streams causing pollution. 2 marks
2. A They do not have … go thirsty. There is also the … habitats becoming damaged. 1 mark
   B Unreliable rainfall can … difficult. Drought conditions can lead to … famine. 2 marks
   C Tensions over water supply can result in war in some … do not have enough to drink. This is what we call 'water wars' … problem in the future, especially in Wales. 2 marks
   D Low water … impact on people. 0 marks

p38 Activity 6

A Pollution from power stations … human activity. Also … there will be more evaporation from lakes which will mean less water is available for drinking supplies. 2 marks

B Reduction in supply due … is a big problem especially with a large number of summer visitors. They should reduce the amount of water available … use less. 2 marks

C Getting more and more water … downstream which can affect villages … the river. This is happening in … live. The local water … much water and letting … result. 3 marks

pp38–39 Activity 7

1. A or D
2. a) Sentence 3 is the weakest because it doesn't link to costs or benefits which are the focus of the question.
   b) B
3. C or B

Topic 5

p40 Activity 2

1. slow 2. deposition 3. concordant 4. crest
5. longshore drift

p41 Activity 3

1. 2 sentences
2. spend 2–3 minutes.
3. a) Example 1: Outline Example 2: Give
4. Example 1: explain Example 2: description

pp41–42 Activity 4

A: Physical processes are described, e.g. erosion with some extended comments, but not well linked to threats on people.

B: Threats mentioned via loss of farmland, but details of coastal erosion are absent.

p42 Activity 5

1. A Longshore drift is a process … prevailing wind. 0 marks
   B Stacks are formed at the … period of time. 0 marks
   C Hydraulic action works … cracks in rocks. It can lead … stack-stump sequence. 2 marks
   D Loose rocks are … then fall off the cliff. 1 mark
2. A Longshore drift … a beach. Waves hit the beach at an angle … deposited. 2 marks
   B Longshore drift is … angle. The waves carry sediment … form a spit. 1 mark
   C A process … down-drift. Longshore drift can cause … their nets. 1 mark
   D A spit … waves. This means … further along. 1 mark

p43 Activity 6

1. Defence 1 B Defence 2 C
2. a) Defence 1: It also settles the water … (steps needed). The bullnose shape throws waves up and back out to sea.
   Defence 2: Groynes – the groynes … barrier. These have … reduce coastal erosion.
   b) Defence 1: Sea wall reduces erosion by 'throwing' waves back to the sea.
   Defence 2: This helps build up the beach which reduces wave energy and erosion.

p44 Activity 7

A Swanage Bay…coastal erosion. Over the years it…damage the coastline. The sea wall…Rock armour is very good at protecting the coast. Soft engineering…cheaper and can include…nourishment. 4 marks

B At Hornsea hard…One benefit has been is that it…the North sea. This can lead…winter months. However groynes…deter visitors. Also the groynes mentioned…a result. Re-…coastal zone management. 5 marks

C Revetments are used at Barton-on-Sea; these are…repaired. Groynes are used to stop longshore drift and act as a good…the coast. Lastly gabions…cliff. These…last very long. 6 marks

Topic 6

p46 Activity 2

a) embankments b) dams c) flood relief channel

a) levee b) floodplain c) meander d) interlocking spurs

pp46–47 Activity 3

1. 2 sentences
2. spend 2–3 minutes.
3. a) Example 1: Outline — Example 2: State
4. Example 1: description — Example 2: definition

p47 Activity 4

A: There is not enough on the types of processes involved in formation, e.g. erosion on outside of river banks, deposition on the inside, etc.

B: It doesn't describe how meanders are formed; instead it says what it is.

p48 Activity 5

1. A Solution is where…dissolved in…tiny particles of sediment… current. 1 mark
   B Attrition is one way in … river channel. 0 marks
   C A 'skipping' motion causes smaller … again. 1 mark
   D Large stones…flow of the water. This is called traction. Faster… conditions. 2 marks
2. A The source of a river flows…down and is quite shallow. 0 marks
   B In the upper course the river is wide and deep, and as you… changes to become shallower and deeper. 1 mark
   C In the upper...mountains. In the middle … deeper but has meanders. In the lower … and very wide. 2 marks
   D Rivers tend … area as you move … sections. They become wider and deeper and are … (less friction). 3 marks

pp48–49 Activity 6

1. Defence 1 B Defence 2 C
2. a) Defence1: Retaining wall and … channel sides are built up to protect the surrounding areas. This has been … Shrewsbury, Shropshire. They work well but can be expensive to build and are unsightly.
   Defence 2: Realignment channels take water away … reaches them. The original … a 'by-pass'. This has been done in many places, including parts of the UK.
   b) Defence 1: They work by diverting the water elsewhere and so reducing the impact in a local area; however they may increase the amount of flooding downstream.
   Defence 2: They work by acting as a regulated store of water so during a potential flood event water can be more slowly released into the catchment.

p50 Activity 7

A Surrounding Sheffield, UK, deforestation … has happened. Heavy … for more living space. The clearing of … increased surface runoff resulting in more flooding. 3 marks

B In Chingford, Essex, people … on the low-lying flood plain in the last 30 years. Rainwater is … floods, heavy rain went … by leaves. Another contributing factors was … .been removed which has reduced the … storm hydrograph. 6 marks

C Tewkesbury is … go through via infiltration and therefore becomes surface run-off. Deforestation stops … trees so it over-flow the river banks. In the Amazon rainforest … increased dramatically. 3 marks

Topic 7

p51 Activity 2

1. climate change 2. biodiversity 3. acidity/alkalinity
4. nutrient cycle 5. aquaculture

p52 Activity 3

1. 2 sentences
2. spend 2–3 minutes.
3. a) Example 1: Give — Example 2: State
4. Example 1: example — Example 2: definition

pp52–53 Activity 4

A: There is not enough detail and/or range of threats.

B: It focuses on costs and benefits of tourism rather than threats.

p53 Activity 5

1. A Overfishing is when people fish too much and there will be less fish, the population … to overfishing. The EU has come up … become extinct. 1 mark
   B When too … be maintained and the … in the longer term, e.g. Tuna. 2 marks
   C Overfishing is … for example, has been … put in place to stop it. 1 mark
   D Fish stocks are a … over time leading to long term decline in fish stocks. 2marks
2. A Coral reefs … in the local area which brings in foreign currency and helps the locals. 2 marks
   B Fishing is a … local markets; also jobs for … medicine source and help protect … buffer zone. 3 marks
   C Corals reefs England … see them, rather than having to travel. 0 marks

pp54–55 Activity 6

1. a) A Climate change is … is increasing. This is linked to acidification which may causes … rarer. If there is acidification … able to grow due to this. Also increasing … flooding. 3 marks
   B Higher temperatures … the pH which can stress some marine ecosystems. Coral reefs … causes bleaching by removing the algae that live with them. Corals are part … around Florida, which can also damage … stressed by human development.
   C Increased temperatures … the UK … stress to fish) as well as increased risk of storm surges … to cooler waters – this will have … the fishing industry. 1 mark

b) A In the North Sea, UNCLOS have been created to set … future catching without long term damage. UNCLOS also … Marine Protected Areas (MPAs) It was hoped … 330ha 'no take zone' – an MPA. 5 marks

B People are … killed and hunted. Also some people are breeding … numbers. This will help … become endangered. 2 marks

C In Australia at the Great barrier Reef they have fishing laws. In St Lucia … marine conservation. The Global marine Species … what really lives in the sea. This will … at a global level. 3 marks

Topic 8

p57 Activity 2

1. snowmelt 2. treeless, <10°C average temperature
3. desertification

Activity 3

1. 2 sentences
2. spend 2–3 minutes.
3. a) Example 1: Give
   Example 2: State
4. Example 1: description
   Example 2: definition

p58 Activity 4

A: Not enough detail and/or range linked to clothing.

B: The last sentence is not about clothing. More detail needed on fabrics / clothing.

pp58–59 Activity 5

1. A People have adapted … cope with the climate. 0 marks
   B Locals have adapted by … this is sustainable. 1 mark
   C In the driest parts of Australia … artesian pumps which are used to extract … deep underground. This technology is important … can suffer droughts. Air pressure … water out through a pump. 2 marks
   D Tourism … way of walking. 0 marks
2. A In deserts, plants have adapted to dry conditions … for water through shedding leaves for example. Animals such as the Red Kangaroo … times of the day to reduce water demand. In cold arctic conditions foxes … having white fur for camouflage. 3 marks
   B People use flat roofs to collect water in dry conditions (e.g. the morning dew). Plants in very cold conditions … reduced their leaf sizes to reduce the amount of water loss by transpiration. 3 marks
   C In polar regions plants grow close … wind damage; they also have … underground water supplies. 3 marks

pp59–60 Activity 6

1. a) A Named region: The Sahel. Solar panels have been installed, this … can work. This is a sustainable source of energy … fossil fuels. Also in the Sahel, agriculture … use of diguettes. These have gone a long way to … areas it has reduced. 5 marks
   B Named region: Africa. Oxfam helped a village in African to build field barriers … soil erosion. This increased … multi-crop framing. This involved planting a range of crops to reduce the risk of single crop failure. This was accompanied … generations. 6 marks
   C Named region: Australia. The coast of … air conditioning. There is a more sustainable clean water supply. 1 mark

   b) A Named region: Australian outback. Life here is … cultures of tribes to change. People are now … with each other (more 'western'). With the climate … more frequent and this is bringing increasing drought and water shortages. 6 marks
   B Named region: Tanzania, Africa. The people of Tanzania have problems with a reliable water supply, however charities … wells and hand-pumps. Tourism has … and see traditional rituals. Infection … prevent being bitten when asleep. 2 marks
   C Named region: Australia. Life for Australians is … there. This is all due to the … the country. Huge droughts … harder as there is a huge lack of water. 3 marks

Unit 2

Topic 1

p62 Activity 2

1. pro-natalist policies
2. birth rate
3. ageing population
4. anti-natalist policies
5. death rate

p62 Activity 3

1. Mark scheme:
   Main/basic point: Birth rate has fallen (1)
   Support/development: because of economic growth (1) Support/development: especially in countries such as China (1)
   Main/basic point: Agriculture less important (1)
   Support/development: so less children needed to work the land (1)
   Main/basic point: Women are having fewer children (1)
   Support/development point: Have jobs instead putting off families until later (1)
2. A 2 marks B 2 marks

pp62–63 Activity 4

A: Talks about how rather than why so misses the focus.

B: Doesn't identify what the 'problem' is.

p63 Activity 5

1. A In some countries governments … families with more babies being born as a result. 1 mark
   B Some poor people need large numbers of children because they need … the land. 2 marks
   C In Singapore there are a number of policies about population … .worked. 0 marks
   D More children … education so they have to stay … mothers. 2 marks
2. A The UK has an ageing population because … opportunities for young people here. 0 marks
   B If the birth rate falls then the average age of the population is likely to rise. 2 marks
   C Some older people have retired to Spain which obviously … population. 2 marks
   D Death rates have gone up because of AIDs and other diseases. 0 marks

p64 Activity 6

A In China they have a one-child policy which has been forced on people who are punished … families that go along … their kids. 3 marks

B China introduced the one-child policy in 1978. It offers rewards to … been sterilised. 4 marks

C China's one child policy has reduced birth rate by about half in 30 years. Other countries have just encouraged families to have fewer children such as Singapore which had a campaign … were enough, whether boys or girls. The smaller … better education. 4 marks

D There are many ways in which government might try … their policies e.g. Singapore. Governments can use punishments as in China or rewards. These can be many different things. Some might be better education and others might be higher or lower taxes. In China … modern China. 2 marks

p65 Activity 7

1. B and C
2. a) Sentence 1 b) A

p66 Activity 8

1. A and D
2. a)

Sentence	Order of usefulness
1	3
2	2
3	1

   b) Sentence 1

Topic 2

p67 Activity 1

Words in following order: faster, resources, shortages, famine, society, helped, economic, growth, population, technical, necessity, invention

pp67–68 Activity 2

1. Boserup's theory
2. non-renewable resources
3. sustainability
4. Malthus's theory
5. renewable resources

Activity 3

1. Mark scheme:
   Main basic point: Inventions make things more efficient (1)
   Support/development: ...such as car engines (1)
   Main basic point: Some resources are replaced by others that are less damaging (1) Support/development: ...so solar power/wind power replace oil (1)
   Main basic point: New ways of recycling (1)
   Support/development: ...such as biogas which saves use of wood (1)
2. A 2 marks B 2 marks

pp68–69 Activity 4

A …it is too brief – what is it people want?
B …it repeats the question and doesn't say why it is rising

p69 Activity 5

1. A Malthus's theory … of resources. So trouble will happen in a society. 1 mark
   B Poor people have … food to go around. 0 marks
   C This says that population grows fast. However we are smart … GM foods. 1 mark
   D Population grows faster than food supply. So famines and war … prevented. 2 marks
2. A Named resource: Oil
   The demand for … them all the time. 0 marks
   B Named resource: Coal
   Coal is very dirty and doesn't...global warming. So other...used instead of it like oil. 2 marks
   C Named resource: Oil
   We are running out of oil. Many oil fields have already run dry because demand has gone up so fast. 2 marks
   D Named Resource: Oil
   Oil is running out so we cannot produce as much. An example of this is the USA. 1 mark

p70 Activity 6

A Technology … technology. This is Boserup's theory. An example of this...food production. 4 marks
B Many people think … the problem of 'peak oil'. We are running out of oil. We depend … to develop fuel from water but it is very expensive at the moment. 3 marks
C There are many problems that result from … might help. An example … that this won't work. 1 mark
D We are running out of many different … run out. Oil is a … are easy or cheap to develop. 3 marks

p71 Activity 7

1. a) Remove Sentence 1 because it is background information, it isn't a problem in itself
   b) Replacement sentences C or D
2. a) The weakest sentence is Sentence 1
   b) The best replacement is Sentence A

p72 Activity 8

1. A and D
2.

Sentence	Order of usefulness
1	1
2	3
3	2

3. B

Topic 3

p74 Activity 2

1. retirement migration
2. the 'rush for the towns'
3. sustainable cities
4. re-urbanisation
5. the rural idyll

p75 Activity 3

1. Mark scheme:
   Main/basic point: Overcrowding (1)
   Support/development: poor housing/sanitation, etc. (1) may add example city (1)
   Main/basic point: High demand for work (1)
   Support/development: few jobs available (1)
   Main/basic point: May cause social problems (1)
   Support/development: migrants may be different religion or racial group (1)
2. A 2 marks B 2 marks

p75 Activity 4

A: Only one way asked for but this answer offers two with no support point
B: It needs some detail of 'upgrading'

p76 Activity 5

1. A If too many people move into cities it can all become difficult. Prices of houses can rise which is good for some people but not for others. 1 mark
   B Young people have … jobs are there. 0 marks
   C House prices might rise as demand rises. This can … Olympics area. 2 marks
   D Rural areas lose population … enough jobs. This can lead to … and small towns. 2 marks *(Examiner comment: This is an unusual response but it is a fair point about impacts.)*
2. A Lots of English villages have falling populations. The people who l… population is ageing. 2 marks
   B There are many … to solve than others. 0 marks
   C More second homes … people to buy houses. An example of this is the Lake District. 1 mark
   D Many young people have left rural areas of India. This causes … behind. 1 mark

pp76–77 Activity 6

A Urban living spaces are in … reasons. Many parts of London are popular…finance and business. Other urban areas have also… Manchester. 2 marks
B The growth of Mumbai has been…rural areas. All the best jobs are in cities and that is why people arrive. They live in shanty… rather than their dream. 1 mark
C Some large cities … more housing too. Urban areas provide more…available than in rural areas. 4 marks

pp77–78 Activity 7

1. a) Remove Sentence 1 because this idea is covered better in the next sentence.
   b) Replacement sentences A and D
2. B and D

p78 Activity 8

1.

Sentence	Order of usefulness
1	1
2	2
3	3

2. B It gives a clear link to sustainability.

Topic 4

p80 Activity 2

1. the Clarke-Fisher model
2. green employment
3. deindustrialization
4. brownfield sites
5. rural diversification

pp80–81 Activity 3

1. Mark scheme:
   Main/basic point: Involved in research and IT (1)
   Support/development: Such as producing software (1)
   Main/basic point: Often found near universities (1)
   Support/development: example such as Cambridge Science Park or Silicon Valley(1)
   Main/basic point: Employs a small % of total employment (1)
   Support/development: about 3–5% in the UK (1)
2. A 2 marks B 2 marks

p81 Activity 4

1. A: It doesn't make a comment about the environment.
   B: Not enough on the environment or on employment change.

p81–82 Activity 5

A Green employment is … environment in some way. An example would be people who work in jobs … environment. There are lots of … development. 3 marks

B Green employment is employment in farming. Jobs in farming … which uses less chemicals. This is obviously … because less damage is done to it. Nitrates can wash off … water which isn't good. 2 marks

C Green employment covers … to improve sustainability. An example is working in developing alternative … hydrogen fuel cells. Many car companies are spending money to do this. Another example would be work on recycling such as Singapore's NEWater scheme. 4 marks

pp82–83 Activity 6

1. a) Remove Sentence 2 b) A or C
2. A and D

p83 Activity 7

1.

Sentence	Order of usefulness
1	2
2	4
3	3
4	1

2. A

Topic 5

p85 Activity 2

1. Green consumerism
2. Eco-footprint
3. Sustainable transport

p85 Activity 3

1. Mark scheme:
   Main/basic point: They recycle waste (1)
   Support/development: example or detail of how they do this (1)
   Main/basic point: They have well developed public transport (1)
   Support/development: impact on reducing car use and eco-footprint (1)
   Main/basic point: They insist on 'green' building laws (1)
   Support/development: example or development of same
2. A 2 marks B 2 marks

p86 Activity 4

A: It is not quite right and too narrow an answer
B: The answer is true but it is not a definition of eco-footprint

p86 Activity 5

1. A Cities that have many manufacturing industries … cities that don't. 1 mark
   B Some cities … waste produced. Other cities have tried to reduce the use of cars. 1 mark
   C Cities can recycle if governments encourage it. This reduces the … land required. 2 marks
   D Not all cities are sustainable. Las Vegas has to import water from … Lake Mead. 2 marks
2. A In Toulouse they have developed a metro system which … cars in the city. 1 mark
   B A government could … altogether. This … would be very unpopular with the people. 1 mark
   C Barcelona has good cheap public transport … introduced a scheme to hire bikes. 2 marks
   (Examiner comment: These two ideas are closely related but just about different enough.)
   D Local governments could encourage people to walk … subsidies. 1 mark

p87 Activity 6

A Singapore is a city of about 6 million people all crowded into a small island. They have pursued … controversial ones. Their most famous policy is the congestion charging which … helps the environment. 3 marks

B Cities like Barcelona have spent a lot of … environment. So has London. In London the Bedzed … energy consumption. There are also schemes to improve … people fitter. 3 marks
(Examiner comment: Talks about two cities and can only be credited for one.)

C If people install … energy consumption will be reduced. This can be helped if people are given grants for … carbon dioxide emissions. This is helpful for the … global warming. There are some cities … An example is Cubita. 4 marks

p88 Activity 7

1. A and D
2. a) strongest sentence 4 because it is the core reason
      weakest sentence 1 because it states the obvious and is not relevant
   b) A

Topic 6

p90 Activity 2

1. sustainable management
2. rural depopulation
3. second homes
4. rural diversification
5. the changing global economy

p91 Activity 3

1. Mark scheme:
   Main/basic point: Distance from services (1)
   Main/basic point: Not enough jobs (1)
   Main/basic point: Not enough variety of jobs (1)
   Main/basic point: Expensive to travel/move around (1)
   Main/basic point: Poor transport (1)
2. A 2 marks B 2 marks

p91 Activity 4

A: Doesn't say where people are leaving from
B: The answer is true but the question is asking to define depopulation not why it happens

p92 Activity 5

1. A Some rural areas become depopulated … decline, such as farming. 2 marks
   B The growth … everyday to work. 0 marks
   C In western China people are leaving rural areas. They migrate to … variety of jobs. 2 marks
   D Many rural areas in Africa have depopulated. This is because of civil war. 2 marks
2. A Planners have … ignore local wishes. 0 marks
   B An example is schemes … cost-effective boreholes in Mozambique. This helps local farmers and slows down depopulation. 2 marks
   C Governments may have schemes for distance learning. In Iceland … regions that are very remote. 1 mark (Examiner comment: *This answer doesn't spot the 'restriction' about the develop**ing** world. Worth a mark because of fair basic point.)*
   D Planners have encouraged micro-credit schemes such as the Grameen Bank. They have also developed the roads and power supply to remote regions. 1 mark

p93 Activity 6

A Rural areas close to … negative impacts from urban areas. If a region is in commuting range of the city … shops and schools suffer. Level 3 5 marks

B Tourists can damage the environment. In the New Forest they often cause fires and kill … Southampton and London. Foreign visitors are also quite common. Tourists bring … also bring problems too. Level 3 5 marks

C As cities grow they can … ways. Not all of these ways are good and … needs of the visitors. Sometimes the needs … environment. An example of this is Scotland. Level 1 2 marks

p94 Activity 7

1. B and D
2. a) strongest sentence 4 or 6 weakest sentence 3 b) A

Topic 7

p96 Activity 2

1. bottom-up development
2. urban core and rural periphery
3. sustainable development
4. top-down development
5. economic development

p97 Activity 3

1. Mark scheme:
   Main/basic point: Rural development that meets the need of the present (1)
   Support/development: without damaging the local environment (1) Support/development: without making it difficult for future generations (1)
   Main/basic point: Development that preserves the local environment (1)
   Support/development: Example of scheme such as biogas/ firewood (1)
2. A 2 marks B 2 marks

p 97 Activity 4

A: Needs a bit more detail or another feature, e.g. central control.
B: The answer is true but the question is asking to define top-down development

p98 Activity 5

1. A Local communities are … decisions. However some of them may benefit with jobs. 1 mark
   B The Three Gorges Dam … project. These are very expensive … successful. 1 mark
   C Top-down … local people So sometimes they don't take into account local needs. 2 marks
   D Top-down projects often mean that … local people. 1 mark
2 A Local communities can be … development. This is because bottom up … technology and not expensive material that cannot be serviced. 2 marks
   B Bottom-up development … usually make the plans. The Grameen Bank has made … local communities. 2 marks
   C Bottom-up development … cheap to establish. There are many examples in Africa. 1 mark

pp98–99 Activity 6

A Ethiopia is one of the world's poorest countries with most people earning less than $2 a day. There are many efforts to help people with bottom-up development plans. An example is FARM Africa helping with … improve schools and other facilities. Level 2 3 marks
(Examiner comment: No disadvantages are mentioned but quite good on advantages.)

B Bottom up projects in Bangladesh have helped local communities. In villages close to Dhaka the Grameen Bank … groups of five borrowers. However the country obviously needs some big projects … large areas. In particular … Sunderbans. Level 3 6 marks
(Examiner comment: A good answer. Especially like the 'however' that points out a big disadvantage of the local schemes.)

C Bottom-up projects have many advantages. Local communities like them because they have a part in the plans … themselves. Top-down projects … consult local communities – this was true of the Three Gorges Project in China … flooded valleys. Level 3 5 marks
(Examiner comment: A little short on detail but has advantages and disadvantages and a little bit of data.)

pp99–100 Activity 7

A and D

p100 Activity 8

1. B
2. A and C

Topic 8

p102 Activity 2

1. global shift
2. outsourcing
3. transnational corporations
4. the 'new economy'

p102 Activity 3

1. Mark scheme:
   Main/basic point: Outsourcing of services (1)
   Support/development: so finance and business operates as a global network (1)
   Main/basic point: Manufacturing moving to NICs (1)
   Support/development: creating jobs in manufacturing in countries such as China (1)
   Main/basic point: New methods of communication (1)
   Support/development: so new jobs in tertiary and quaternary sector (1)
2. A 2 marks B 2 marks

p103 Activity 4

A: It misses the point about 'trans**national**' and talks about only one feature.
B: The answer is true but only talks about one feature.

p103 Activity 5

1. A Outsourcing takes … an example is China. 1 mark
   B Outsourcing happens when … make money. 1 mark
   C Outsourcing is when a TNC … country – an example is Nike's factories in Vietnam. 2 marks
   D TNCs have many … one of these. 1 mark
2 A The new … quaternary sector. 0 marks
   B Manufacturing jobs … China and India. These have been … countries such as Britain. 2 marks
   C Jobs are … changing jobs many times and having to learn … employment changes. 2 marks

p104 Activity 6

A In many developed countries … employment. There are about 31 people working in the UK. In recent years … coal mining. In developing countries … places like China. Level 2 4 marks
(Examiner comment: Makes a mistake saying over 31 people (31 million!) but some good ideas. Looses the focus at the end. Just a bit too narrow for Level 3.)

B Jobs have been lost in manufacturing industry. In 1950 there were 35% employed in jobs like machine tools, car manufacture, shipbuilding and the UK was a big exporter. Today it is only 15% working in these types of jobs and many … been 20,000 people. Level 2 4 marks
(Examiner comment: Excellent detail but very narrow focus on just one industry. Needs a wider range of impacts.)

C Very big changes have taken place in rich countries. The growth of TNCs has changed completely where things are made today. Many more women … tax as well. Level 3 5 marks
(Examiner comment: Gets a bit too concerned with the rights and wrongs. A little more local 'detail' instead of the comments about bankers would give this 6 marks. It is a little short on detail but has advantages and disadvantages and a little bit of data.)

p105 Activity 7

A and C

Activity 8

1. A
2. A and C